Tell T[illegible] What You Want

Laverne Merritt-Gordon
(with Beau Grosscup)

Ames | Berlin | Lemgo

Culicidae Press, LLC
918 5th Street
Ames, IA 50010
USA
culicidaepress.com
editor@culicidaepress.com

TELL THEM WHAT YOU WANT.

ISBN-13: 978-1-68315-024-4

Library of Congress Control Number: 2021931007

Cover design and interior layout © 2021 by polytekton
Cover image of tree © www.gograph.com / Ambassador806

This book is dedicated to my beloved sons Bryan and Brandon,
my husband Denman, and my entire family and friends.
My deepest love to my sister Francis, 'the warrior'
who literally and physically saved my life.

Table of Contents

Acknowlegement

We would like to thank everyone who took valuable time out of their busy lives to make telling this story a reality. We are specifically indebted to Sandi B. Ver Linden, Anne Hamilton, Joe Russo, Rose Ann York, Janis Dutton, and members of the Osher Lifelong Learning Institute writing class (CSU, Chico) for their careful reading of the manuscript, thoughtful advice, encouragement and honest critique. Thank you to Valerie Elliott of the Smith Library of Regional History (The Lane Libraries) for her valuable historical research. Collectively you have enriched the telling of this story. Most importantly, our heart felt appreciation goes to Laverne's cousins David Churchman and the late Charles 'Chucky' Warren "for being the first to encourage me to write my story."

Prologue

My tree is powerful, knowing, caring, protective, and loved me. I grew with and from my tree.

Laverne Merritt-Gordon
(December 23, 2020)

"I know you Bobo Grosscup," a smooth, slightly husky voice says from above me. I look up into the neighborhood kids' favorite climbing tree. A small dark figure dangles from a limb. Squealing with delight, it lets go, lands softly on two feet and into the rest of my life. She is a scrawny, yet muscular, dark chocolate toned girl I have seen once or twice on the elementary school playground. Flashing a big smile, she announces, "I'm Bernie, I live over there."

Flushed with pride, she points to a house across the street belonging to one of my Negro paper route customers. She starts up again—spitting words out a mile a minute.

"I know you 'cause I know your brother Pete. He's in my class. And your sister, I know her too. She's a horse girl. She beat me in a footrace over at the stables, but not by much. She's fast, but a lot older. Bet I pass her up soon. I heard about your mother too. My mama, not my real mama, her name's Mrs. Charles, she talks about her, how she tries to do good things for folks all the time. And Bobo, you deliver the paper to the houses on this street, even to us Coloreds. I see you from the window and—"

"Okay," I cut in. I am staring into the biggest, brightest eyes I've seen in my ten years. "I get it. Somehow you know me, but I don't know you. Why are you so keen on my family? You spying on us?"

"I am not a spy! I'm just interested in what's going on. Mrs. Charles calls me 'Little Miss Curiosity.' Says it's a good thing. That's how I know you. I like it when you bring the paper."

Putting her hands on her hips, she licks her lips and says, "I can read, you know. I love to read. Can you read Bobo?"

"Of course I can read. "I'm in the fifth grade. But I didn't think the Charles had kids, at least ones that live with them. They're sorta old people."

"Well I—I mean we—we are pretty new here," she stammers. My reply seems to have hurt her a bit. A frown crosses her face as she says, "My brother Walter and me, we used to live near Hamilton. But not any more." The big smile returns as she announces, "We're in Oxford now with Mr. and Mrs. Charles, and some other kids."

"I see," I say, looking back at this little Negro girl whose mood changes in a second. I sort of understand what she means about the Charles taking her in. I've heard a little about foster kids.

"You want to play tag Bobo?" she asks, swinging up into the lower branches. "Bet you can't get me!"

"Naw, I gotta go home to get my bike. Got my route to do."

"Okay," she yells, climbing further up into the tree. "I'll be waiting here. Don't forget our house. I get to read the funnies first."

Walking home I keep wondering what happened to this happy little girl and her brother. Why aren't they living with their real family?

It takes fifty-some years of friendship before Bernie tells me her secrets.

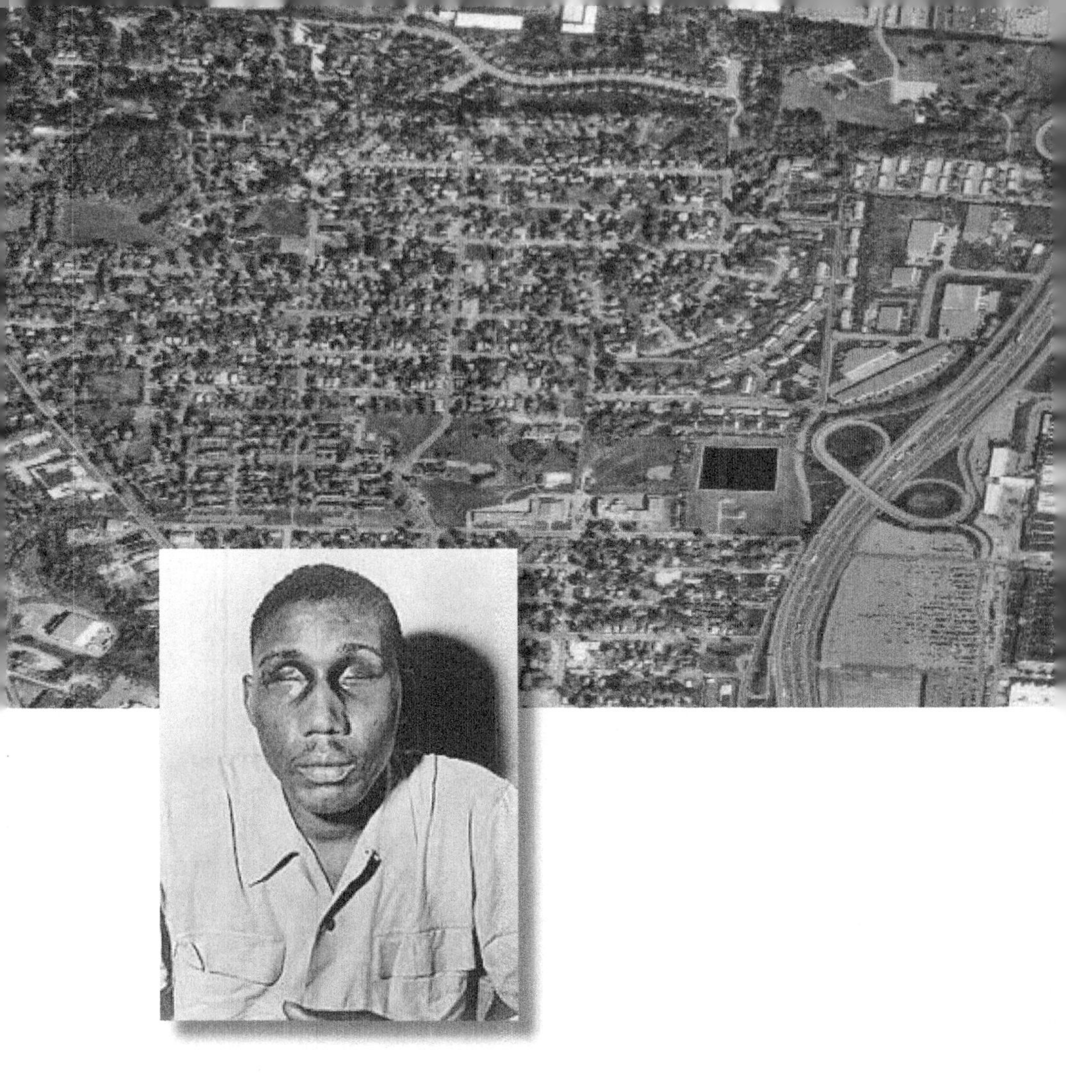

1946, February 14. Isaac Woodard, a Negro veteran of WW II is beaten and maimed by white South Carolina police. Woodward is on his way home after being discharged from the US Army. The beating ruptures his cornea, leaving him permanently blind.

1946. The village of Lincoln Heights in southwest Ohio is finally incorporated and becomes the first primarily Negro self-governing community north of the Mason-Dixon line. Attempts to incorporate in 1939 were stalled by white resistance, land grabs by neighboring white communities, and lack of support from Hamilton county and Ohio state officials, and leave the town, once known as the Black Wall Street, with only ten percent of its' original land and no industrial tax base.

Chapter 1

Devil House

I'm Bernie and I'm seven, almost eight years old. A social worker named Helen just picked me up from the Hamilton Ohio hospital and is taking me to live in some town called Oxford. Riding along, I look out of the car window. Everything is so beautiful: white clouds, green grass, and lots of big trees whose branches seem to touch the blue sky. We pass a field with some cows. I've never seen a real cow before. I really like the black and white ones. Being out in the country is so different from my New Miami neighborhood that it scares me a little. But I've been scared before, really scared for a long time. Scratching at my belly scars through my new blouse, I remember back best I can.

*

I was born in Lincoln Heights, a Colored part of Cincinnati, Ohio on March 1, 1946. Family folks say when I came out of Mama my skin color was light pink. I'm told that pink lasted until I was three years old. I really don't remember. But I sure am black now! Not blue-black like some Africans; there's brown mixed in, but black enough—too black for some people.

My aunts say that when I was born, my parents were caught up in a family fight. A couple of years later, my daddy just disappears. Somehow my mama gets pregnant and my brother

Walter comes along. Mama takes up with a man named Johnny McVay. My grandfather gives Mama money to build a house on his property in New Miami, the Colored part of Hamilton Ohio. All seven of us, including Johnny McVay, move in. Mama says he's our stepfather.

Right away, Johnny takes over everything in the house, especially us kids. He gets mean and nasty. He hits us, shoves us around and screams, "Do this, do that—do it now!" We go from one bruise or scratch to another. Worst of all, he plays with our head, keeps us guessing, scared of what's coming next in that house. Sometimes the three older kids, depending on their 'situation' with Johnny, run off for a while. Walter and I are only three and five, just babies, so we are stuck. Johnny goes after our mama too. Every night they sleep, fight and do whatever in a locked bedroom. I don't want to think about that. In the winter, we kids sleep squeezed together on a cold laundry room floor. On warm nights, Johnny puts us under the house in what is sort of a basement. It's really just a wet, dark box with a few stairs to the outside. Johnny makes his two German Shepherds sleep with us. I guess they are supposed to watch us, make sure we don't sneak out into the fresh air. Sleeping with us, the dogs get to like us more than Johnny. It's why I love German Shepherds.

Everyday, Johnny wakes up angry and comes to get us. This Saturday is the same. "Black gal, git them brats up now! Stuff's gotta be done," he yells from above the basement stairs. 'Black gal' is Johnny's name for Franny, one of our older sisters who tries to protect us young ones. She is very brave, standing up to him, trying to save us from his mean stuff. It makes him really mad if someone gets in his way. He always says he will 'get' Franny later. I'm sure he does. Franny never says, but she doesn't have to. Her body is covered with bruises and cuts. I promise myself that when big enough, I will be a big sister 'Franny' to Walter and whatever babies come along.

"I'm doing it," Franny shouts back. She wakes us. We crawl up the stairs and sit on the grass looking at him with sleepy eyes.

Scared, we wait for him to tell us what to do. "Puke," he says. That's his name for me. I don't know why. "Grass been growing. Git them scissors an' start cutting if you want to eat. You want to eat today Puke?" "Ye—Yes sir!" I stammer, now wide-awake. My tummy is flapping around inside. It always gets that way when I'm scared—and Johnny really scares me! Hearing my voice, Bull, the big shepherd growls at Johnny. "Shut up mutt!" Johnny yells, throwing a rock at him. Since the dogs began to bark at him, Johnny keeps rocks handy. Bull growls and barks back at Johnny, just like Franny does.

Cutting the lawn with dull scissors, that's my chore today and most summer days. In the winter, Johnny makes me run naked out in the cold and snow to see if the car tires are flat. They never are. What Johnny really likes to do is get us kids up in the middle of the night to wash down the house walls that we scrubbed only a few nights before.

Going to get the scissors in the kitchen drawer, I hear Johnny go after the other kids, calling each by the special name he gives us. As I say, Franny is 'Black gal.' I am 'Puke.' Coreena, another older sister, he calls 'Yella gal.' Little Walter is 'Devil.' That Devil name for Walter—that's not right. That's our name for Johnny and his house. Johnny has a whole lot—I mean a whole lot of 'put down' names for older brother Billy, who is growing up fast. I think Johnny is scared of Billy, scared if he pushes him too hard, knocks him around like he does the rest of us, that Billy will haul off and whack him upside his head. I can't wait for that! So Johnny just calls Billy names. Mostly, they are about him being some kind of 'sissy' like a girl, what they call queer. Billy is almost thirteen. I bet he's the first of the older kids to run away forever. He talks about it. Franny too, but she wants to take Walter and me. She says the law won't allow it. For sure, Johnny and Mama won't.

Outside, I get on my knees and start snipping at the grass. Hopefully, I'm doing a good job, because getting anything to eat is up to Johnny. He decides if we did enough work, or as he says, "Got it right." If so, we eat, if not, we don't. He tells Mama what food to fix, how much and when to serve it. He locks all the food in a cabinet and refrigerator in his bedroom so even when he and Mama are off to work, we can't get to it. Nobody knows for sure, but the older kids think Johnny's starving us on purpose to get rid of Mama's kids.

Even if Johnny lets us have food, there is never enough. Sometimes when he is gone, our aunts, Mama's sisters, bring food over, cook it up real fast and get out of there before that devil man comes back. Sometimes we have to stuff down half cooked or raw meat. Otherwise we steal food from neighbors' houses and nearby grocery stores. At one store it's so easy to steal a little food I think the store workers want to give it to us. Most days, we dig into garbage cans. Yes, I eat out of garbage cans. Yes, I feed little Walter out of garbage cans! It's how we survive.

When we're not doing chores, Walter and I follow our brother and sisters around, staying close to them, hoping for protection. Most of the time we hang onto Franny 'the warrior.' There are no friends, no toys, nothing. I don't even know what a doll is. People just talk about it. I don't go to school either. That's weird because Mama says I am her one kid who is always trying to learn things and tell everybody about them. I do! When Johnny isn't around, I beg the big kids to let me see their books, help me read. I love to learn big words and try to use them. I have some 'imaginary friends' I talk to and even make believe the chickens in the yard are my students. If Johnny ever sees me 'pretending,' for sure he won't like it—tell everybody I'm a crazy fool. He already slaps me for talking 'fancy pants.' I don't care. Learning things is what I like most.

*

Today starts like most others when Johnny and Mama aren't at work. One by one, Johnny gives us kids a job. Of course, he makes our chore as hard or stupid as he can, like me cutting the lawn with scissors. He loves messing with us.

I cut grass all morning. Finally, Franny calls, "Bernie, come and eat. Mr. McVay says you can get to it again tomorrow." I get up off my aching, grass-stained knees and go to the kitchen. A plate of meat and bread scraps, left over from Johnny and Mama's meal, is on the floor. Johnny says tables are for humans, so we sit on the floor and gulp down the scraps.

As usual, after their lunch, Johnny and Mama are 'resting' in their bedroom. Still starving, one by one we kids sneak away to search the neighborhood for food. I always take little Walter with me. As the oldest of the youngest, it is my job to look after him and the twin babies. It doesn't matter whether we are Johnny's real kids or not, he doesn't like any of us. He is even hard on his twins Jonni Mae and Jonni Lou. They're born a year after we move into that Devil House. When Jonni May was two or so, Johnny slugged her in the mouth so hard he knocked some front teeth out. He told Mama, "Damn kids get in the way."

Johnny even goes after Mama right in front of us. When he does, we all bunch up in a corner, hugging each other tight, waiting for the screaming and hitting to stop. Only once do I see Mama get back at him. She is in the kitchen ironing. Johnny comes in cursing and starts screaming at her, calling her bad names. Mama keeps on ironing. I guess she isn't paying enough attention for him. He reaches out and slaps her hard in the face. She quickly lifts the iron, puts it on his chest and holds it there. "Hey bitch!" he yells, falling back. "You trying to burn me?" Mama waves the iron at him and says, "Your shirt was wrinkled." I know he will get back at her, that later something very bad is going to happen in that bedroom. But still, I'm happy she got him this one time! It's like she put in a lick for us, for all of us especially since she did it with the clothes iron. Of all the things he beats us with, the worst is the iron cord. It leaves big welts that turn into scars that last a long time, if not forever. Got mine.

Our mama, supposedly before she met Johnny, she didn't take anything from anybody, a 'cause fighter' is what our aunts say. Now she's different. There's something about Johnny that has gotten to her. He says the Bible made men the 'House King.' Mama believes that for sure. I just wish she would protect herself. Sometimes I see her walking around the house sobbing; mostly after a night of curses and screams from the bedroom keep us awake.

Johnny says he'll whip us good if we talk about what goes on in his house. With us little kids he doesn't have to worry, since we don't know any different. The big kids lived with our real daddy for a while so they know what Johnny does isn't right. Franny says they try to get the word out, but nobody believes them. Besides, Johnny is really good at fooling folks, especially at the neighborhood church. He's a deacon and sings in the gospel choir. To the church ladies, who he 'plays' with his smooth talk, 'Deacon Johnny' is doing God's work. Who's going to believe any bad things about him, especially, as he tells folks, from a bunch of 'no count' kids? Johnny makes sure Mama is on his side. He does his spell on her, hitting and cursing her, then says he's sorry. He does that a lot. It works too.

Johnny is always saying, "What happens in a man's house is nobody's business." It must be true, as it's very hush, hush around the neighborhood. Everybody just minds their own business. Officer Jeffery Keane, the white policeman who walks the streets, never stops at anyone's house to ask about anything, never mind go inside. So while Johnny is messing with us kids, worse could be going on all over the place. Franny says it is for sure at little Margie Davis' house.

Our aunts want Mama to leave Johnny. So do the Bartles, our next door neighbors. They have three kids. Johnny doesn't allow us to play with them. Mrs. Bartles, Vera Jo, also sneaks food over to us. She and Mr. Bartles probably know some of what goes on here. Vera Jo and Mama talk a lot, mostly when the men aren't around. Franny says it's how women survive, having women friends. Johnny hates that! He cusses Vera Jo something awful. He's always yelling at Mr. Bartles, "Get hold your damn woman—nigger!"

Even as a little kid, my brain wonders why anybody puts up with Johnny, especially Mama. Why can't she get free of that devil? Maybe it's what folks call her 'constitution,' feeling she should be here for her kids. That's nice, but still, for her kids, everyday is doing what 'Deacon' Johnny wants or getting your butt beat—or worse. It takes the worse happening to me that saves some of us in the end.

1952, March 21. The Moondog Coronation Ball in Cleveland Ohio is shut down after one song for fear of a riot caused by overcrowding. It is the first time the performers are racially mixed and perform before an integrated audience. It is generally thought to be the first 'rock and roll' concert.

Chapter 2

Fire!

Billy gets burned first. He is watching the fire that we kids, mainly Walter and me, have to keep going almost every day in the backyard. We start the fires with either kerosene or some black gooey stuff called 'coal oil.' In winter, Johnny often locks us out of the house during the day, so having a fire helps us stay warm. Mama uses our fire to heat water for washing clothes.

Somehow, sparks set Billy's pants on fire. Scared stiff, he watches as the flames crawl up the backside of his leg. Sister Coreena quickly grabs the washing tub and throws water on the flames, putting them out. Billy spends a month in the hospital recovering from bad burns to his leg. He never comes back to that Devil House.

Two months later I get burned. I must have gotten too close to the fire because all of a sudden flames burst out on the front of my little blue nylon dress. I panic. Screaming, I run around the yard as fast as I can, trying to brush away the flames with my hands. Franny screams, "Stop Bernie! Stop running!" I keep running in circles, faster and faster, fanning the flames. My whole belly is cooking. The flames are licking at my chest, burning my arms. I pound my fists at them, yelling for help. "What do I do? What do I do? Help!! Help me somebody! Owwwwwah—it's bur—burning me up!" Something hits me from behind, knocking me to the ground on my burning belly. The flames die down. I flip over and the flames blow up again, going even higher. Out of the corner of my watery eyes I see Franny bounce up off the ground. Throwing somebody's ragged coat on me, she jumps on top. Pressed against each other, we roll over and over in the dirt, trying to put out the flames with her body. It works! Finally, the flames are out. Franny got to me fast, but not fast enough. The flames burn up my dress and bare belly. I pass out before any real pain starts, not knowing that Franny 'the warrior' has saved me again.

*

I wake up in Hamilton's Mercy Hospital. All I see is white. The walls are white, so is the bed. I am wrapped in white material, gauze they call it, from my neck to my knees. Three white men in white coats are standing by the bed. I am the only black thing in the room. Coming from where I do, I'm not used to that.

"Well hello Miss Bernie," one of the men says. I come to know him as Dr. Grant, the lead surgeon. "We're glad to see you are awake. How are you feeling?" The pain is sky-high. "It hurts," I moan. "My stomach, my legs, they hurt." I try to sit up. The belly pain goes deeper. "Aaggggggg!!" I scream. "Careful," Dr. Grant warns, pushing me back gently with his gloved hand. "You have some burns. But we are going to take care of them and you." He looks at the other white men in white coats and smiles. They smile and nod back at him.

I don't know where I am or what happened. All I remember are flames racing up my front. Glaring at them, I ask, "Mama, where's my mama? Franny? Is W—W—Walter okay? Ouuuuuch!" It hurts to talk. "Your mother is here at the hospital. The rest of the family is okay and home," Dr. Grant replies. "We have to pay attention to you right now. That's what your mother wants most and so does everyone else."

*

Over the next year, I get to know Dr. Grant, the other doctors and their team of nurses very well. They tell me Franny saved my life with just seconds to spare. Now they are trying to save my body. Usually burns are first, second or third degree. I think I am beyond that. As far as I know they don't have a name for it. The burns on my stomach go the deepest, exposing my nerves to the air and infection. The surgeons do a skin graft using some kind of tool to cut the good skin from my back. They put it on my belly, hoping it will attach itself and grow. For days I am wrapped up like a mummy to keep the burns moist and the new skin free from infection. I am curious about what's going on, so I keep asking lots of questions. Everybody tries to answer best they can. Even the doctors say much of what they are doing is new to burn medicine.

The first graft doesn't take. They do a second one with a new kind of cutting tool, so they tell me. They also build a sling type thing that suspends me over the bed. This allows them to pour a fluid on me all the time, some kind of saline solution I'm told.

The second skin graft works! I am very, very lucky to have these doctors and nurses. It takes months of surgery, treatment and a lot of pain for me to heal. I finally leave the hospital, walking on my own two feet. I have an inch and a half deep of scar tissue over most of my belly. It looks like brown crinkled plastic paper.

Before I leave the hospital, my doctors give us the bad news. The burns have damaged me for life because I don't have many stomach muscles left. 'Crippled' is the word they use. I will probably have back pain since my back muscles must work overtime, trying to do what stomach muscles do. They say I can never have children and probably won't be able to do anything really physical. Cancer is a real possibility. I will need hospital check-ups every five years. The burns and grafts are very painful, but to me what the doctors say about my future hurts even more. I love those doctors for what they did for me. But when they tell me what I can't do, it—it really frustrates, in fact makes me mad! It's Dr. Grant who catches this girl's temper. "You still don't know me, do you? After all this time, you still don't know what I am about? You'll see. I will do whatever I want. I'll run if I want to. And fast too. I'm a very fast runner. I'll climb trees. I—I'll even have a baby if I want to!" Dr. Grant smiles and gently says, "Of course you will Bernie. I have no doubt. I'm just trying to say be careful. Don't get your hopes too high." I glare back at him. I shake my head up and down at fast as I can and yell, "You'll see. I'll do whatever I want!"

Still smiling, Dr. Grant pats my knee and says, "I'm sure you will Bernie." After he leaves, I lie back and think, Wow! That was some stuff coming out of your mouth! I really don't know what I will be able to do. Not have a baby? Really? No running? Jumping? A cripple. Me?

I've had a year in the hospital to think about things, especially about me. I may be young, barely seven, but I have a lot of what they call pluck. Yes, I am plucky! That's what made me yell those things at Dr. Grant. And thanks to Franny and the doctors I have another chance. No way will I spend my life being a cripple. No way!

I leave the hospital and go back to that Devil House. Things are different. Billy, Franny and Coreena ran in the middle of the night to family in Lincoln Heights. I don't blame them. Otherwise things are the same. Johnny is just as mean, maybe more with no big kids around. I'm the oldest, so it's up to me to protect Walter and the babies. I have to be Bernie 'the warrior' now. Somehow I have to fight that devil man. Am I scared to death? Yes! My tummy is constantly twitching inside. What scares me most is that Johnny knows about my burned belly. One punch could rip my scars wide open, bringing back that awful pain and more surgery. Still, I am going to stand up to his nasty stuff best I can for little Walter and the babies—myself too. That ole' fire almost got me for sure. But I'm still here!

1953. The Highlander Folk School in Monteagle, Tennessee changes its focus from running workshops on class and labor issues to civil rights. Labeled a 'communist training center' by its critics, the racially integrated school begins to train many civil rights activists including Rosa Parks, Septima Clark, Anne Braden, Martin Luther King Jr., James Bevel, Hollis Watkins, Bernard Lafayette, Ralph Abernathy and John Lewis.

Chapter 3

Belly Out

With the big kids gone, Johnny thinks he can do 'whatever' to us small ones. He gets even meaner, especially about giving out food. Somehow he gets wise our aunts are 'visiting' when he is out of the house. We are all so bony! I begin to look really weird with my skinny muscular arms and legs and a scarred up potbelly. Of course, Johnny has fun with that. He tells me, "Hey Puke, you're so ugly, no boy ever gonna want you."

One day, everything changes. Johnny has taken Mama to the South somewhere, Alabama I think, to visit some of his relatives. Johnny's brother Harold is left in charge of Walter, the three babies and me. He and his wife Thelma live in a little trailer on the edge of the property. 'Uncle' Harold is beating up on his wife too.

Just like Johnny, Harold wakes us early in the morning, gives us jobs and promises we can eat if we do right. All morning he curses and pokes us from behind to work faster. Finally it's noon and Harold is nowhere in sight. Walter is very hungry, me too. "C'mon Walter," I say, "We need to find some food."

Leaving the twins in charge of the new baby, we walk over to the neighborhood store. Walter picks up some chewing gum at the checkout counter to sidetrack the worker. I quickly shove two bananas into my armpit under my coat. Walking to the counter I say, "No candy today Walter." Taking him by the hand, we walk out of the store. Halfway down the block we peel and eat our bananas. A moment later, I feel something strange going on in my stomach. The next thing I know I wake up on the ground, open my eyes to see Vera Jo and Mr. Bartles frowning down at me. They look scared. "Hey child, you with us?" Vera Jo whispers. My head hurts like crazy. There is yellow-green-black vomit all over. "I—I don't know," I say, wiping wet chunks of banana off my face. "Wh—what happened?" Suddenly I panic and ask, "Where's Walter?"

"Walter's right here," Vera Jo replies. Smiling down at me, she pulls him out from behind her skirt. "He's just fine, came and got us. He's trying to not get sick. Holding it down so far." Then, Vera Jo turns to Mr. Bartles and growls, "Frank, go find Officer Keane. Enough is enough!"

*

I end up in Mercy Hospital's white world again. They say I have something called malnutrition. That's why my belly sticks out from my skinny body, like I'm fat. They say I'm 'distended.' I thought it was because of my burns. That's what Johnny said. But after a nurse shows me *National Geographic* pictures of starving African kids, I know for sure my belly is 'distended.' With scrawny arms and legs and poked out bellies, they look just like me. I don't care what Johnny tells everybody; that is not normal. I'm lucky my scars didn't rip open!

The police start looking for Johnny and Mama. Several days later they find them in Alabama. Meanwhile, I am being kept warm, given sips of water and a little sugar. Later, I will get real food and hopefully eat my way back to looking normal. I hear some patients complaining about the hospital food, how awful it is. I want to scream, "Man, you don't know anything. I can't wait to eat some."

*

A week later, Johnny walks into my hospital room. Looking around, he quietly shuts the door. The scowl on his face tells me he's up to no good. My scarred belly starts fluttering. I'm quaking—

shaking, terrified! Johnny walks over to my bed and grabs my arm. Squeezing it hard, he leans his face close to mine. His rotten breath almost makes me vomit, but I'm too scared to not look at him. "Listen Puke girl," he snarls. "You be quiet. Don't you say nothing 'bout nothing. You do—you start running your mouth I will get you for sure. You hear me? You get it Puke?" Shaking all over, I stammer, "Ye—ye—yes sir Mister—"

Suddenly a huge white man comes flying out of the closet. I don't know how he got there, but he did. An even bigger white man comes through the hospital room door. They grab Johnny by the armpits, spin him around and shove him out of the room. It all happens so fast! I'm shocked and scared stiff. The only thing moving is my big belly, flapping around inside like crazy! "Wha—what's happening?" I yell out to nobody. A nurse comes rushing in. "It's all right Bernie," she says, reaching for my hand. "Don't worry, everything is over. It's all right now."

"Oh, th—that's good."

I'm still scared, but need to talk. I take some quick breaths and blurt out, "What's going on with Johnny, I mean Mr. McVay? Where are they taking him? Who are those men? Where is my mama? Tell me what's going on?" "I don't quite know, Bernie," she answers, pulling the covers up over me. "Someone will be right here to explain, I'm sure." Turning to leave, she looks back and says, "I'm just sure you are safe now."

A few minutes later Vera Jo and Mr. Bartles arrive. They tell me the man in the closet was a detective. So was the other man. It was a set up. When Johnny threatened me, the detectives were ready. "Johnny and your mama have been arrested," Vera Jo says quietly. Her eyes are wet. "Arrested? Mama arrested? Why?" I howl. "She didn't do anything bad! Wh—what about Walter, the twins, the baby? Where are they? What will they do to Mama?" Vera Jo looks down at me. Finally, she smiles and says, "Everybody is okay Bernie." Taking my hand in hers, she leans close and whispers, "And so are you, our little big girl."

1950, May 29. In Oxford Ohio, the public swimming pool opens as a legally integrated facility after the Oxford Ohio branch of the NAACP wins its legal suit against the Village of Oxford.

1953, January 16. In Oxford Ohio, *The Oxford Press* editorial reports that restrictions ended in 1951 for Negros to attend Miami University's McGuffey Experimental School. No Negro has yet to attend.

Chapter 4

State Kid

A month after Johnny and Mama's arrest, I am out of the hospital and on my way to Oxford, a small town a half hour from New Miami. As I watch the trees and cows fly by, the social worker Helen says I will be staying in something called a 'receiving' home until somebody wants me for real. She also says I have to go to school. I have no idea what that means, so it scares me. What really scares me even more is at seven years old I am alone without my mama, Walter and the older kids for the first time in my life. When I ask the social worker about them, all she says is, "Don't you worry Miss, they are okay."

Arriving in Oxford, we turn onto a street with huge trees. I love to climb trees, getting as high as I can. Looking down makes me feel a lot safer—far away from the stuff I'm dealing with on the ground. With lots of big trees, Oxford is already heaven to me—so far. We pull up in front of a nice looking house. A tall slender man and slim woman are standing on the porch. Right away they seem different from most other Colored folks. They are older for sure, and the way they stand; it's different, very dignified. I guess they know I'm coming. I climb out of the car and walk to the house. Three steps up and I am on the porch. My twitching belly tells me I'm nervous. The woman, who is very elegant up close, reaches out her hand and says, "Hello, Miss Bernie. Welcome to our home. I am Mrs. Charles and this is Mr. Charles. We are glad you are staying with us." "Thank you Ma'am," I whisper, shaking her hand and then his. It's easy to do since I'm shaking all over anyway. "Thank you for bringing her, Helen," Mrs. Charles says to the social worker. They obviously know each other. "Of course," Helen responds. Turning to me, she says, "You will like it here Bernie. Mr. and Mrs. Charles are wonderful people." We all watch as social worker Helen drives off. "Well, Bernie," Mrs. Charles says, taking my hand. "Come inside. We'll show you the house and your room. The other kids aren't home yet, so you will meet them later."

"What kids?" I blurt out. "Is Walter here? The twins?" Mrs. Charles looks down at me. Sadness on her face, she says, "No, your kin aren't here. You don't know these kids. Like you, they have come to live with us for a while. They are good kids. You will like them."

I don't know what to think. Lots of questions pop into my head. There are kids here but not Walter? If I'm here, why isn't Walter? Who are these kids anyway? Why are they here? Will they like me? What if they don't? Tears start rolling down my cheeks. Mrs. Charles pulls a tissue from her blouse. Dabbing my wet face, she says, "Come Bernie, you must be hungry. Mr. Charles has fixed us a nice lunch." My tummy twitches harder. I think, oh no, the man controls the food here too! Mrs. Charles is waiting for me to follow her, but I can't move. A picture of Johnny's locked up refrigerator runs through my head. Then I think, heck, if some man or anybody is handing out food, I'm not saying no! I look at her and say, "Yes, thank you Ma'am. But—"

Mrs. Charles interrupts me. "What is it child? Our lunch is waiting."

I turn, point across the street and ask, "I'm wondering. Before we eat could I climb that tree?" Mrs. Charles squeezes my hand, walks me toward the front door and softly says, "First things first, Miss Bernie. That oak tree isn't going anywhere, and right now there are more important things to do." It's my first lesson about life with Mr. and Mrs. Charles. First things are first. Things go in order.

At lunch I discover more things. Mrs. and Mr. Charles, they're both in charge of the food. There is lots of it and boy is it good. And for the first time in my life, I get to sit at a table to eat.

*

I start my life at the Oak Street house as best I can. I still don't know anything about my family, where they are or what has happened to them. That is really tugging at my belly scars for sure. My first night, Mrs. Charles tucks me in bed and explains that I am now something called a 'Ward of the State.' But it is only temporary. I try my best to understand, but I can't. I meet the Charles' other kids, Belinda, Janet and Donnie. They are all very nice but quiet. We don't talk much about why we are here. We just know for now we are in a safer place. As 'State kids' we all are wondering who will want us and why? Both Donnie and Janet had mean foster parents and were sent back to the Charles. From what they tell me, people take in kids for all kinds of reasons, some not so great. They tell me to be on the lookout for police cars, because the State can come snatch us up at any time. They tell me to always sit by the window, especially at school. That way if I see a police car I can run and hide, in a closet, behind a bush, in a tree, anywhere. So, I do. In the meantime, I'll just enjoy living at Mr. and Mrs. Charles' house as long as I can. After Johnny and all that, it's pretty easy. Doing what they ask, helping out with chores and being nice to the others gets smiles, compliments and little hugs. And I get permission to climb those trees across the street.

Unlike Johnny and Mama, yes I miss Mama for sure, but with Mr. and Mrs. Charles there are no fights, no hitting, no secrets. Watching them, it just seems they like each other a lot. If that is love, I'm all for it. For sure, Mrs. Charles is in charge of the house and us kids. After Johnny and the other men I'm used to, that seems really strange. But having a nice woman in charge, I can get used to that real quick.

To me, Mrs. Charles becomes more elegant and smarter each day. The other kids say she went to college. How she did that, I don't know. Maybe, if somehow I get to know her better, she will tell me. I'm too afraid to ask her now. All I know is, for being so educated she sure is 'down-home.' I want to be just like her when I grow up.

Mr. Charles is out working a lot. But when he's here, he goes around quietly, always fixing things. He sort of cackles and has twinkly eyes. He seems to like us kids. I hope—I mean I will marry a man just like him.

The Oak Street house is the best place! The Charles, they talk to each other all the time, and talk about lots of interesting things. I love to listen in and learn things. But there's no messing around when things need to get done. And, when we act like kids, they seem to understand pretty well. They just talk to us about where we are, who we want to be and how to get there. It's too good to be true. I mean, I get it, but I don't get it. For the first time in my life I have my own room, a bed to sleep in, a table to sit at and plenty of food to eat. Best of all, I am around kind people. I don't feel completely safe, but more than ever before, that's for sure. Hopefully my next stop, wherever it is, will be the same or better, hopefully. The only thing spoiling things is little Walter. My brain goes crazy thinking about him. Where is he? Who's looking out for him? Will I ever see him again? Why isn't he up in this tree playing tag with me?

*

A few weeks after my arrival, I'm in the backyard planting a few of Mrs. Charles' iris bulbs. Suddenly little Walter comes racing around the corner of the house! Seeing each other, we both scream.

"Bernie!"

"Walter!"

Walter runs and jumps into my arms, knocking me to the ground. I eat that boy alive with kisses. He tries to squeeze the life out of me with his powerful hugs. We roll and roll around the yard, tearing at each other with tears and screams. I can't get enough of that boy! Exhausted, we finally stop and sit up. Mrs. Charles is standing on the back porch. Smiling down at us, she says, "I see you know each other."

I have always had a special thing with Walter. Maybe it's because, in the line-up of Mama's 18 kids, he was born right after me. I don't know. I am close to many of them, at least those I know. But he always gets my 'protection thing.' Sometimes I call him 'Baby Huey' because he is the strongest little kid I know. My sister said 'Baby Huey' is in the Popeye cartoon book and is extra strong. Walter is like that. When he arrives at the Charles, he is just five years old. But he can lift Mrs. Charles up off the ground. She'll be in the kitchen and he comes up behind her, wraps his arms around her legs and boosts her a few inches off the floor. Mrs. Charles cracks up and begs, "Put me down Walter, put me down."

From the moment Walter was born, everybody starts calling him Popeye. It's because he has the biggest, most beautiful eyes popping out of his head. But I never call him Popeye. To me, he is Walter, my 'Bubba.' Always has been, always will be.

Now Walter is here with me on Oak Street. He seems to love being at the Charles' house. We both are still afraid of starving, so I sneak food from the table and hide it in my room for Walter to eat later. Sometimes Mrs. Charles finds where it's hidden. She seems to get what's going on. Instead of getting upset she just quietly says, "You don't have to worry, there will always be plenty of food for you here." And there is. I still hide food for Walter, less than before but—. Even when we wet the bed at night, Mrs. Charles just says, "You never mind, just part of growing up." Still I don't like pee in my bed, so I try to stay up all-night. I can't so—. I know Walter loves being with me again. He races around all the time, smiling and laughing. Every day he sneaks up and yells, "Love you Bernie!" "Love you back Walter!" I shout.

So here we are having a wonderful life for the first time. Walter and I run around like crazy, climbing trees like cats, playing games with neighborhood kids, just having fun. I'm pretty happy and I know Walter is too. Hopefully we can stay that way and together, wherever. It's why I keep watching out for those police cars.

1954, May 17. In Brown Versus Board of Education, the United States Supreme Court rules that segregation in public schools is unconstitutional. In Ohio, the ruling serves as a death knell for local school districts' 'unofficial' segregated school system for Negros and whites.

1955, March-October. Claudette Colvin, Aurelia Browder, Susie McDonald, Mary Louise Smith and Jeanette Reese refuse to give up their bus seats to white women in Montgomery, Alabama and are arrested. In February1956 all except Reese are named as plaintiffs in Browder v. Gayle, the bus desegregation case. On December 1, Mrs. Rosa Parks refuses to give up her seat to a white passenger on a public bus. She is arrested, tried, and convicted of disorderly conduct and violating a local ordinance. Prominent members of Montgomery, Alabama's Negro community launch the Montgomery Bus Boycott to protest the segregation of Negros and whites in public transport.

1955. After three years of integrated marches at the front gates and a NAACP suit, Cincinnati's Coney Island Amusement Park is racially integrated. Due to a political compromise, the park's Sunlite swimming pool and Moonlight Gardens dance floor remain open to white customers only.

Chapter 5

Choosing To Live

The State took us kids away from Johnny and Mama, but they are still allowed to see us. Sometimes, Mama comes to Oxford. That's really nice. Mama's very different away from Johnny and his Devil House. I wish she'd leave. Other times, Helen the social worker drives us to New Miami, back to that house for an afternoon visit. Sometimes Johnny is there, scowling at us from the porch. It scares me to see him. I can tell he wants to get at me. But then he heads off somewhere, probably to church. So, we get to spend time alone with Mama and the babies. It's fun being around them a little bit without that devil man.

When social worker Helen drives us to New Miami, we talk a lot. She tells me, that all the time we lived with Johnny and Mama, they weren't married. The State told them that if they got married, they could probably get us kids back. So Mama and Mr. McVay got married. I can't believe it! Get married and you can have us back? What about Johnny's messing with us, whipping up on us for nothing all the time? The man tried to starve me—us to death. Don't they know why I was in that hospital? Can Johnny really hide all that from the State people? I think, of course he can. He can fool anybody about anything, especially since he says he is 'God's servant.'

*

One morning, Mama arrives at the Charles' house with our two social workers. Along with Mr. and Mrs. Charles, we all gather in the living room. Helen, my social worker, talks first.

"Bernie and Walter, today is an important day for everyone. You get to decide where you want to live. Your mother wants you to come back and live with her and Mr. McVay. You may if you want to. Or you can choose to stay here with Mr. and Mrs. Charles for a little while longer." She pauses, stares at us and says, "Do you understand? Walter, do you understand?"

"Yes Ma'am," Walter says softly. Out of the corner of my eye, I see his whole body twitch. Helen turns to me.

"Bernie, do you understand the choice you have?"

"Y—ye—yes, m—Ma'am," I stammer. I'm in shock. My upper body sways back and forth. My stomach starts churning inside. Outside, I feel my belly scars crunching around like they want to wrinkle up. It happens when I get really scared.

Then Helen turns back to my little brother and asks, "Walter, do you want to live with your mother?"

"I want to be with Mama," he says quickly.

A jolt hits my stomach. I am sure my scars are ripping apart. I stare at Walter, thinking, I can't believe he said that. He wants to go back to that Devil House? Why? I want to scream at him. What are you doing? No. Noooooooo!

Clamping my jaws shut, I shove the shriek back down my throat. But my brain keeps screaming at Walter. What are you doing? Why—why would you want to? Then it hits me. Of course he wants to be with Mama. He's just a little kid. A sweet, scared little kid whose mama is sitting right in front of him, giving him her best 'I love you' smile.

Mama quickly gathers Walter up onto her lap. I think, no way will he change his mind now. Helen turns to me and asks, "And you Bernie? Do you want to live with your mother?"

I don't, can't answer. My face is hot, burning up. Everybody is staring at me, all eyes checking me out. I'm thinking, why are they asking me this? Why, after all the things he did? I don't like this. It's ridiculous. Stuff begins to fill my head, very bad stuff: awful bits and pieces that are months, even years old, but clear as ever. Swallowing a gob of spit, I think, wow girl, this is serious. Really serious!

I look over at Mr. and Mrs. Charles. They are watching me. Their faces are blank. They aren't helping me, telling me what to do. Why aren't they helping me? Don't they want me here? Trembling even more, I look at my mama. She is so beautiful. I know she loves me—us. She is hugging Walter and smiling at me. His beautiful pop-eyes are bursting with excitement. I know what they want me to say, to do. I stare down at the floor. It seems to be moving up and down, flopping around. Everyone is waiting. Finally, Helen repeats the dreaded question.

"Bernie. What about you? Do you want to be with your mother and Walter?"

I raise my head and look straight into space. My eyes fill with tears. I force my mouth open and try to squeeze the words out.

"I—I don—I don't want—I'm sorr—I ca—can't—"

The other social worker cuts me off. "I'm sorry Bernie, we can't understand you. Please speak up."

I clamp my lips shut, choking back my truth, the truth. I pitch my upper body downward, squashing my face to my thighs, my nose between my knees. I just want to disappear; make myself invisible. But it's not working. Seconds pass, then from deep inside my trembling body, a voice screams, "Get to it girl. Tell them what you want!" I straighten up. Pressing my hands against my tingling belly scars, I scream, "I can't go back there. I—I will never go back!"

I hear, feel my hatred bouncing from wall to wall. Nobody moves or says a thing. In shock I guess. I look over at Mama. Disappointment covers her beautiful face. She hugs Walter tighter, burying his face between her bosoms.

"I'm sorry Mama, but—" I mutter, choking back my tear-filled truth. My brain is full of doubt and fear, and questions. What did I just do? Should I take it back? Am I stupid? No, I'm not stupid. I know what it means for Walter and me. My little brother, my soul mate, I just tore us apart again. I don't want to, but no way can I go back to that Devil House; Johnny's messing.

Helen breaks the silence. "Bernie, I am sure your mother, indeed all of us would like to know why you can't go with her. Can you, would you tell us?" I look at her and then around at all of them. Sobbing, I manage to spit it out. "Be—because I want to go to college. And I like it here. I love Mrs. Charles and Mr. Charles. I love Mama. And I love my brother. But I just want—can't—"

I stop talking. I don't want to say anything else, don't want to hurt any more feelings. I look around. Everybody looks mixed up, like something I said doesn't make sense. Then Mama, my blessed mama starts talking.

"I want her to stay. I would love to have her with me, but I want her to stay. She can get things here I can't give her. She needs a lot of things. I know what those things are because I wanted them for myself. I will never be able to give them to her now. She—she is my special child."

I—I can't believe what Mama just said. Did I hear right? My mama said that? Really? She wants me to stay? I'm special to her? My heart's pounding. I don't know what to think, how to act, what to say. Then I suddenly get it. The hardest choice in my life, I made it. Told them what I want. And Mama knows what I want. She gets it, wants it too. Wants it for me!

Mama, her big beautiful eyes full of water, walks over, pulls me to my feet, grabs me in a bear hug and silently rocks us back and forth. Letting go she whispers, "See you soon B."

As Mama goes about her good-byes, I grab Walter and hug him as hard as I can. My tears drip all over the top of his head. Mama returns, and taking Walter from me, heads out to the car. From the porch, I watch her get in the driver's seat. On the other side of the car, little Walter climbs onto the runner and opens the door. He turns and waves to me.

"Love you Bernie," he shouts. I wave back at him.

"Love you back Walter. Love you more!"

My little brother disappears into the car and is gone. Standing on the porch, all I can think about is my Bubba. I just know something bad—awful is waiting for him. But, I can't be there right now or maybe anymore for him. I just can't! For the first time, I have to do for myself.

A month later, a miracle happens. Mr. and Mrs. Charles decide to take me and the other kids into their home to be our Mama and Daddy Charles. Their Oak Street receiving house is now a boarding home. I'm still a State kid, but as long as the Charles want me—and I behave, I get to stay here. All of a sudden my life is really worth living, and more. If only Walter could—.

1950, May 4. In Oxford Ohio, seventy-five percent of the Miami University students who vote in student elections favor ending racial discrimination in Oxford's restaurants. Coffee Pete's and the New England Kitchen's white owners are the first to sign the Campus Interracial Club's statement pledging that "Eating places in Oxford should be open to all persons regardless of race."

Chapter 6

Little Miss Curiosity

Oxford is like being on a new planet. I'm just a little kid who doesn't know much about anything important. For sure, I haven't heard about being white, brown, yellow or whatever. I think it's because, except when I was in the hospital, I have only been around Colored people. Johnny would curse about the 'white devils.' But he never let us go far from that house, so I never really knew what he meant. To me, the devil is the devil. To me, Johnny is the devil. And he is Colored for sure.

Miami University is in Oxford, so students are all over the place. Most of them are white, so for sure that's weird. At first I think Oak Street is on campus because some student dorms are just two blocks up. But it isn't. There are kids on Oak Street and a few of them are Coloreds. There's Rita Neal and Tommy Naydock and us State kids. That makes our street different. On the rest of the streets the houses are full of white people. What's really strange is that the Colored cemetery is in the middle of all the white people. It's on Chestnut Street, just around the corner from my house. We walk by it everyday on our way to school. At first I wonder, where do they bury all the white people? Soon I find out that the white cemetery is on top of a beautiful hill a few blocks away from Oak Street. Mama Charles says white folks pay more to be buried there than in the Colored cemetery. I think that's a good deal since they get to look at some big cliffs called the Bluffs and two streams full of fossils and some Indian arrowheads. Our paperboy Bobo Grosscup's family owns the land, so it is okay for us to be there. I already know how to scoot up and down the Bluffs without falling. And there are big beautiful trees to climb way up, sit and daydream.

My world on Oak Street is pretty small. There's the Neal family, the Naydock family and the Charles, all Colored. Living right next to us is a white professor's family. They are Russian and have three kids. The oldest one, Henry, is a brat, always up to stuff. One night he put his radio out of his bedroom window and blasted it as loud as he could so nobody can sleep. Mama Charles put a stop to that real quick. The worst thing he does is pick his nose and eat boogers right in front of us. Two other white professors' families live on our block. All three white families and their kids, except for Henry, are very nice. He is mostly okay. He just likes to eat his boogers. Yuck!

So far, I get along with everyone on Oak Street. Even though I'm the new kid, I'm in and out of the white and Colored folks' homes all the time. I am having a great time doing what kids do, playing games like tree tag and hopscotch. We play softball in the big field across the street. Sometimes there are cows in the field. They belong to a farmhouse on the corner next to the Charles. I've never been close to a real cow before. We try and ride them. There's a mean old bull too. No way do I get on that bull! Later, some machines pick up that farmhouse and move it off somewhere. The university bought the empty lot, tore down some white folks' shacks at the end of the block and put up married student housing. That changes things for sure. There are no more poor white kids to play with. No cows to ride or bull to tease and run from either.

Things are different at school. The Colored kids tease me about living on whitey's side of town. That's the word they use, whitey. I don't know enough to pay any mind to that. Being new and a State kid, white and Colored kids tease me a lot, testing me I guess. If it gets rough I fight them, go after all of them if I have to. I hear I'm getting known as a fighter. I'm not a bully, but I'm not afraid to fight. Sometimes fighting makes me feel better inside, like I've done something important, got back at somebody. I even got in a fight with Lulu Jones, and she's a State kid. Guess we both had to take out what Mama Charles calls our 'locked up anger' on somebody. Fighting another State kid, that didn't make sense so we're friends now. One time I even beat on Petey Grosscup, Bobo's little brother, on the school playground. I don't know why, nothing he did or said—just did, felt like hitting something I guess. Ju—just mad!

*

My busy life on Oak Street keeps me from knowing what goes on in other parts of Oxford. But soon, I hear the Colored kids at school talk about 'the difference,' about the south side and north side. I don't know what that 'side thing' means. Then I discover that Oxford is built on a hill. At the top is High Street, where the stores are. It divides Oxford into a north side and a south side. Mama and Daddy Charles do all their business on our side, the south side. We do go to the Elm Street Christian Church just across High Street. We drive there on Sundays, but come straight home after church. The other side of town, it's weird to me.

There's another thing going on that really bugs me. At the end of the school day most of the Colored kids get on a big yellow bus and drive away. I don't see them until the bus brings them back to school in the morning. They're not around on weekends either. They just disappear. For all I know, they're going to the edge of the earth. I ask a couple of friends about it. All they say is, "We go over to north side." My guess is they go to a town called North Side.

Mama Charles calls me 'Little Miss Curiosity.' She's right. So one day I decide to ride that yellow bus to see where it goes. I'm not too scared 'cause the bus brings the kids back safe every day. I'll get back home somehow, even if I have to walk. I can do that. It's too late to tell Mama Charles or any Oak Street kids what I'm doing. I'll tell them when I get home.

I walk to the bus with my new best friend Billie. I told her I've never ridden a bus before, so she takes my hand. We hurry past the driver, find an empty seat and sit down. Five minutes later the bus, full of noisy kids, takes off. Without stopping, it goes up to High Street, crosses and heads down a hill. At the bottom it turns onto a partly paved street with big holes and no sidewalks. I see a bent street sign hanging down on its post. Billie says we're on Sycamore Street. The bus stops every few houses to let kids off. Some of the homes are pretty nice. Not big or anything fancy, just nice. Others remind me of the run down shacks in New Miami. There are only Colored people on the street and in front of those Sycamore Street houses. It's just like New Miami.

We reach Billie's house. Getting off the bus, I look around and say, "So, this is where all you are. You don't live in another town, just on the other side of Oxford, the north side."

Billie gives me a weird look and giggles, "Where did you think we lived girl?" I don't tell her I thought they fell off the earth and somehow got back on to come to school.

We hang around Billie's house talking and laughing. Several kids stop in, so it's fun. When it's time for me to go home, Billie walks me down to the corner of Sycamore and Campus Streets and tells me, "Bernie, if you follow Campus Street all the way across town you will be home. You will know where you are when you get to High Street."

"You mean my Campus Street is the same one on the north side?" I ask. Billie chuckles, "Bernie, you really are lost. Not just Campus. All the streets are the same on the south and north side. They just cross over the hill."

That did it for me. Finally talk about 'north side' and 'south side' starts making sense. It seems like a small thing, but for 'Miss Curiosity' it is a big deal. Now I have an even bigger world to explore. Still, walking home I am confused. I'm excited that I found out where those buses full of Colored kids end up. But I'm disappointed that I didn't know about the north side earlier. With all these kids around, it would be a lot of fun to go over and hang out. I also wonder; why do the Colored kids live on the north side, but go to school on our side of town? And then after school they get on a bus that takes them back? Why don't some of them stay and play with us over here? I bet Daddy Charles would give them a ride home if they need it.

Near home another 'little kid' question pops up. If most Coloreds lived on the north side, why are they buried forever on the south side?

I am late when I get home. I go to the kitchen to set the table. "Child, where have you been?" Mama Charles asks. "We were worried about you." I tell her. She hugs me. Then, turning back to her cooking, she says, "Okay, now you know, but don't go over there again."

"Don't go? Why not?"

"Because South side whites and Colored are not welcome there."

"B—But I was—"

Mama Charles cuts me off. "Listen to me, Miss B. Just don't go. Now set the table please."

I know better than to keep on. But, as I gather up the silverware and plates I wonder, what's that all about? My first taste of the 'difference,' and it's more confusing than ever.

1957, August. William and Daisy Myers, a Negro couple, purchase a home in the all-white suburban neighborhood of Levittown, PA. They are threatened with racist harassment and mob violence. The Myers refusal to sell their house results in an injunction and criminal charges being filed against the racist harassers. Daisy Myers is hailed as 'The Rosa Parks of the North.'

Chapter 7

Getting Educated

Wow, things are exploding all over the place. The TV is full of news about what's going on down South between whites and Coloreds. At the Charles house, we all know about a kid named Emmett Till, and what happened to him, and of course Rosa Parks sitting on a bus where she wasn't allowed. Now it's about Coloreds going to white schools, trying to eat at white restaurants and all the trouble that's causing. Mama Charles watches the TV news, shaking her head and muttering, "About time" over and over. The South is far away, but I'm learning it's a dangerous place for Coloreds. It's hard to think about people being lynched and murdered just for being Colored. Mama Charles says it's been going on a long time. Of course, I want to know as much as I can about all that, so I keep asking questions. Mama Charles tries to explain to 'Miss Curiosity' as best she can.

I'm also learning more about the 'difference' in Oxford, in fact all over Ohio. It's different from what is going on in the South, but it is here too, Coloreds and whites being different. At first, it seems really weird to me since Miami University is full of smart people. And in school I learned that in the Civil War, Ohio was with the North. We also read about the Underground Railroad. My teacher said more runaway slaves took that train through Ohio than any other state, and that tunnels still connect some Oxford houses. Maybe we'll get to crawl around in them someday. I'd like that.

Okay, but that bus ride to the north side opened my eyes a little bit about what's going on in Oxford, why there are two sides of town. And what Mama Charles said about not going to the Colored part of north side, I really don't like it. All of it is really stupid!

*

I'm just a fifth grade kid, but I want to do something about this 'difference' thing. Sometimes I invite a few friends to walk home with me and hang out at the Charles house. They all say, "No, we need to get back home" and hurry to the bus. I can't get any white friends from Oak Street to go with me to the north side either. Let's just say they seem scared. I have seen Bobo Grosscup playing ball over on the north side. He's older and we don't really hang out, so it doesn't matter to me what that white boy does. Anyway, I really don't like what's going on. I mean, living apart is one thing, but kids not hanging out wherever, that's really weird. I need answers, so I start asking everyone, starting with the Charles. They frown and look at each other. Daddy Charles speaks first. "That's the way it is." "Right now," is all Mama Charles says. So I try my north side girlfriends. Yes, I keep going over there, making new friends. I think Mama Charles knows but doesn't say anything, wants me to find out for myself, I guess. Wow, those girls can really talk about 'the difference.' One day, they sure make me listen.

Several of us are hanging out at Billie's house, fixing up our hair and bopping to Chuck Berry's new record. Tired, we sit down to rest. I ask, "Why don't you all ever stay over with me on the south side? We can do this at my house too." My friends stare at me in disbelief. Then Billie blurts out, "Girl, don't you ever notice where you aren't welcome?"

"No, I guess not. Like where?"

"Like wherever whitey is," Billie hisses. "Like on the south side and especially uptown where all the shops and stuff are. High Street is whitey's street. They sure don't like us in their stores.

Colored stores are all down here on north side, like Knox's on Sycamore."

"Hey girl, you ever get into those white peoples' houses down on south side?" my friend Janet asks.

"Yes, of course I do, On Oak Street I go into my neighbors' houses sometimes. They like me to—"

Billie cuts me off. "Of course on the Charles' street. Anywhere else? You're always down at the Bluffs. You ever been in the Grosscup's house? Bobo's been over here to our houses a few times. You go over to his?" Before I can answer, Billie goes on. "You know his family has that jockey statue out in front of their house? Confederate flag up out back too."

"N—no, I don't," I stutter. "So?"

Billie is amazed. She starts in on me. "So? Bernie, you really don't know racist families put those jockeys and flags up to let everybody know how they feel about Colored folks?" Surprised, I say, "But the Grosscups, they're not like that. At least I—"

"Yes," Billie interrupts. "I know them. Pete is in my class. He told me they didn't want to be racist, but they didn't want to give up the statue. So his dad painted the jockey's face and hands white. I told him, it's the jockey that sends the message. I guess they don't get it."

My head is spinning. I'm wondering why Bobo's family would do that, when Miranda, another friend, speaks up, "You even know there's a public swimming pool in Oxford, Bernie? Everybody's supposed to be able to use it, Colored folk too. Supposedly it was opened to us a few years back, around 1950 I think."

"Yeah," I scoff. "I do know there is a pool. It's out on Contreras Road. Mr. Charles talks about a family called Kollman running it. Mr. Charles knows Mr. Kollman. He's an Olympic track coach or something at the university."

"At least you know that," Miranda laughs. Billie breaks in.

"Have you ever been swimming out there Bernie? Or can't you swim."

"I can't swim," I say. "I like wading around in the creek at the Bluffs. But I want to learn to really swim. I was thinking about riding my bike out there to see what that pool is like. Maybe I could take some swimming lessons there."

My friends start howling and slapping hands. "What's wrong? What's so funny?" I ask. Billie is the first to stop laughing. Frowning at me, she says, "Girl, don't count on getting swimming lessons at that pool. They don't want us; say once Coloreds get in their pool all kinds of grease and dirt will be in the water. Makes the pool all nasty and stinky, they say. You don't—"

"Really?" I interrupt, getting upset. "Really? They say that? That doesn't make sense."

"Of course not," Billie replies. "But, that's what they tell everyone. They say to get rid of our grease and dirt they would have to drain the pool and scrub it down everyday, sides, bottom, everything. Everyday. Be a lot of trouble, they say."

"So, don't even think about going out there B," Miranda says. "Yeah, supposedly it's for everyone, integrated is what whitey calls it. But we sure aren't welcome. I mean we have a right to swim there but—"

"Yeah," Brenda growls, "Those Colored boys can run and jump for Miami's track team all they want. But swim in Kollman's pool? No way."

Frustrated, I try something else. "Well, I have been to the university pool, it's called the natatorium. That's where Mr. Charles works. He is allowed to take us kids there once a week for an hour. And we don't make it dirty or greasy, so I don't know what those people are talking about. I'll just go there for swimming lessons."

My friends all giggle. "Once a week, huh," Miranda snickers. "Bet no white folk in that pool with you."

"No, It's reserved. It's because of Mr. Charles. He says that time is designated just for us."

My friends glare at me in disbelief. "Designated," Billie says. "Designated. That's a good word. Designated just for you. Come on girl. Whitey just doesn't want you swimming with them anytime, anywhere. Girl you—"

A familiar voice cuts in from the back of the group. "They don't want you going to school with them either, if they can help it." It's Sherri, a quiet, really smart girl who I do homework with sometimes.

"What do you mean?" I ask. "Colored and white kids go to Stewart school."

"She's talking about McGuffey!" Billie snorts. "You know, the university-run school that gets kids ready for college. The white professors' kids mostly go there, the up-town store owners' kids too."

Billie stops. A sad look crosses her face as she starts up again. "Bernie, you're always talking about how you're going to get an education; go to college someday. Well good for you. But if you are soooo smart why aren't you going to McGuffey? It's right up the street from where you live."

"I don't know," I reply. "Mrs Charles never said anything about McGuffey. When I got here, all the Charles' kids were going to Stewart. So I just thought the Charles knew—"

Sherri interrupts me. "That's because they're racists. They find ways to keep us out. My dad and mom tried to get my sister and me in. They say we have a right to go. Civil rights folks say so too: been fighting to get us in for years. My mom says Miami people who run the school keep changing things, the rules I guess. I don't quite understand it."

"Right," Billie says. "My dad knows how. He's been to the meetings. It's complicated; something about their student teachers only need to practice on white kids. It sounds funny to me, but it works; keeps us out for sure."

I'm confused and getting mad, but my friends aren't finished with me. "And don't go trying to make money from whitey either," Norma, another girl says. "They won't buy anything from us. I know 'cause I tried. We all tried. Found out, we can only sell stuff to our people on the north side."

"Really?" I reply. "What about Girl Scout cookies?"

"Girl Scout cookies? Why would you want to sell Girl Scout cookies?" Billie asks. "They're pretty lily white—"

Brenda cuts her off. "Doesn't matter; can't sell anything to whitey 'cause they won't buy from us." The rest of my friends shake their heads, agreeing with Brenda. They begin to gather their stuff to leave. I guess my education lesson is over for now.

Frustrated, I head out across town thinking about what they said about selling stuff to white people. I don't believe them. A few months back, I joined Oxford's Girl Scout troop. Everyone in the troop is supposed to sell cookies. I'm the only Colored girl, but so what? I am sure I can sell lots of cookies in my south side neighborhood. Now my girlfriends tell me I can't, or won't.

When I get home, I go straight to Mama Charles for answers. First, I ask about selling my Girl Scout cookies to white folks. "No dear," she says softly. "Just sell your cookies to our people. You'll do fine."

My second question surprises her. "And McGuffey? Why didn't you send us to the best school?" Mama Charles looks down at me. Scowling, she says, "Because that's where the high and mighty send their snobby kids. And nobody's high and mighty in this house."

"Then it's not only for white kids," I say. Mama Charles looks straight into my hope-filled eyes and scoffs, "That too, but we are going to change that."

I'm having trouble believing things are this way. But soon I get a real lesson in this race 'difference.' But even then it's confusing.

*

In the sixth grade, my best friend is Tilly Ann Malas. She's from a country called Turkey. Oh boy, do we love each other! Her family lives in a place called Vet Village. It's a couple of blocks up and off Oak Street. The little green buildings are divided into two small apartments and all bunched together. It's really sort of a little town for Miami University's married veterans. Some foreign students live there too, including the Malas family. Thanks to them, I get to know some people from far off lands. I really like that.

When I turn eleven, Mama Charles allows me to go to the movies with Tilly Ann. Oxford has two theaters, both uptown on

High Street. Tilly Ann has been before, but it is my first time. Mama Charles drives us to the Miami-Western Theater and buys our tickets.

"I will pick you up at 4:30," Mama Charles says in front of the theater doors. She hands us our tickets and says, "You wait here after the movie. Do not go anywhere else, young ladies."

"Yes Ma'am," we reply together. We walk through the lobby and into the dark theater. As we stop to let our eyes see, Tilly Ann says, "In here, Colored people sit on the left side. Whites sit in the middle and on the right."

Well, I don't know anything about white seats, Colored seats, right and left seats. What is that about? I wonder. Before I can ask her, Tilly Ann whispers, "Come sit with me Bernie."

She trots down the aisle, turns into a row of seats in the middle of the theater and sits down. I don't know what to do. I wait at the top of the aisle. I really want to be with my best friend, but she just sat down in white country. Then I think, those rules are probably just for adults. I bet little kids are allowed to sit anywhere. Guessing I am right, I jog down to Tilly Ann and plop in an aisle seat next to her. Holding hands and giggling, we wait for the movie to start.

Suddenly, someone is standing over us. We turn to see who it is. It's a white woman. I don't know who she is, but she sure knows who I am.

"Bernie, you can't sit here," she says firmly. I look up at her. Her face says she sort of feels sorry for me.

"B—b—but Tilly Ann is my best friend and she saved this seat for me," I say. "I want to sit here." The lady frowns and says, "I'm Mrs. Timmich. My husband owns the theater and he sets the rules. I'm sorry, but you have to go and sit over there."

She points to the left side of the theater. A few Colored people are sitting there.

Looking back at her I ask, "But why can't I sit with my best friend? I'll be quiet and watch the movie. Nobody will know." I start to blubber up a little. I don't know what this is all about.

I mean I do, but I don't. Mrs. Timmich stares hard at me. Her pity is gone. "Because I say you can't," she mutters. Her thin lips are so tight they are almost white. I realize she didn't answer my question. Lots of adults do that to me. It gets me very mad. I feel my face getting hot. I think, don't give up girl! Grabbing Tilly's hand, I say, "Tilly Ann is my friend—my best friend. We—we ALWAYS sit together."

Mrs. Timmich glares down at me. Then, after looking around the room, she shrugs and says, "You wait here Bernie." She disappears into the back of the theater. Tilly Ann and I look at each other, grab hands and wait. I'm nervous but hopeful.

A minute or so later, a huge fat man with a puffy face and big cigar clamped between his teeth is standing over me, staring down. Now I'm scared as can be! I don't know what to do except open my eyes wide and point them right back up at him. Finally, he takes the cigar out of his mouth. Flicking ashes onto the rug, he says, "I'm Mr. Timmich. Mrs. Timmich says you really want to sit here. Is that right Bernie?"

As usual, my stomach is churning, making my belly scars itch. I'm scared but know what I want.

"Yes sir, I want to be with my best friend Tilly Ann."

Mr. Timmich looks down at me, a frown covers his fat face. Slowly he takes his eyes off me and looks around the theater. Then, bending down close to my face, he says, "Okay, you can do that." He quickly straightens up, puts the cigar back between his yellow teeth and is gone. I'm in shock. I think, wha—? Did he say that for real? I think he did! I smile at Tilly Ann. She grins back. Giggling, we hug each other hard. Letting go, we straighten out our skirts and stare at the screen, happily waiting. The movie starts. I don't remember much about it. I just know everything is wonderful, that in some kind of way I am freer than I was before. I don't understand it, but I feel something big happened this day.

Riding home, I tell Mama Charles what happened. She smiles, pats my leg and says, "Mr. Timmich is a good man."

Sure enough he is. From then on when I go to that theater, which isn't very often, I sit anywhere I want. But it isn't just about one little kid anymore. Word gets out. Soon more and more Coloreds, mainly Miami students, come to the Miami-Western Theater and sit wherever they want. Everyone else does too.

1958, October 25. More than 10,000 youths march in Washington D.C. in support of integrated schools and to thwart southern segregationists' racist propaganda. Among the marchers are Coretta Scott King, Jackie Robinson, Daisy Bates, A. Phillip Randolf, Bayard Rustin. Harry Belafonte leads a delegation of students to the White House to meet President Eisenhower but are turned away.

1958. Ohio Governor C. William O'Neill issues an Executive Order directing the Ohio State Employment Service to reject discriminatory employment requests.

Chapter 8

Going Uptown

Despite what happened at the movie, my friends are right about the race 'difference' or racism as they call it, in Oxford. Maybe Mr. Timmich's letting anyone sit where they want in his theater is his idea. Maybe he is for Colored rights. I don't know. It sure seems that decisions like his and what I see on TV are beginning to change things. Also Mama and Daddy Charles talk a lot about the civil rights protests going on all over the country. Still, the longer I live in Oxford, the more I find that the racism that I—we deal with, is everywhere, but out of sight. 'Subtle' is what the older kids call it.

Even at twelve years old, I know it's not against the law for Coloreds to eat at Oxford's uptown restaurants, but few do. Like the public swimming pool, we know we aren't welcome. Billie's older sister Nadine says that The Huddle, the best restaurant in town, makes it so clear that no Coloreds ever dare to eat there. Nadine can really go on about it too.

"Now, if you are Colored, Chinese or whatever, they will hire you to do the dirty work in the back, the kitchen or dish room, for not much money. And of course, you only come and go through the back door. And you never work out front. Only white workers serve food to customers at The Huddle. Only white workers get tips."

Virginia, another older girl, tells me another thing. "It used to be Coloreds weren't served in any Oxford restaurant. It's better, but still we don't just sashay into any place we want. If you do, the looks you get are saying, "And just what do YOU want in here?" All over town you get that 'you're not welcome' thing."

Okay, I'm getting it. But it seems that part of why I am so ignorant—man I don't like that word, about Oxford's race 'difference' is because of Mama Charles. White people, who know her or know of her, treat her with respect. And that's a lot of people. I'm finding out Mama Charles is way ahead on things, not just as a Colored, but as a woman too. She is a business lady. She has a garden behind the house. Everyone wants flowers from her, especially her gladiolas. She has beautiful 'glads'. She also bakes wedding cakes for everybody. Everywhere, she is treated with respect. I guess they are thinking, oh this is the nice lady we get our cakes from or the lady who works for us. I think they see her as a human being. It's hard to tell. I just know that when we kids are with Mama Charles, and Daddy too, boy, things sure are different, especially up on High Street.

*

One day, I find out how real this is. I go uptown by myself to shop for sewing notions. I make things, sewing and such. I go into Cutlers, a little department store where Mama Charles and I shop together a lot. I want to buy something with my own money. At once a white woman worker, who knows me, starts following me all over the store, acting like I'm up to something, maybe stealing. I don't know. She keeps asking me questions.

"Can I help you? Can I help you? Do you know what you want?" Each time I tell her, "I am okay, I know where to find things." Even when I find something I need, she keeps going after me. "Is that what you want? Pretty expensive, can you afford it?"

I do not like that! Finally, I go up to Mr. Cutler, the owner. He is standing at the cash register. As polite as I can be, I ask him, "Excuse me Mr. Cutler. Why is your helper woman following me around, bothering me? You know my Mama and Daddy Charles. So why are you letting her do this?" Mr. Cutler glares down at me. In a gruff voice he asks, "Are you sure you have money? Do you have enough money to get what you want?" Shocked, I think, well of course I don't have everything I need. With that lady bugging me, I couldn't get it!

As usual, when I get nervous or bothered, what's left of my stomach muscles start to twitch. And boy, am I bothered now! I don't care anymore. I just want to get out of here! I show him the little ribbon I've chosen.

"Yes, I have enough money," I say, handing him a folded up dollar bill from my sweaty hand. Frowning, he makes change and shoves it in my face. I grab it and quickly leave the store. I am really disgusted!

A few days later Mama Charles and I go back to Cutlers store to get what I need. As usual, Mr. Cutler is behind the cash register counter. When he sees us enter, a big smile spreads across his face and he says, "Oh, how are you today Mrs. Charles? And Bernie, how are you? Look at you, all grown up."

I want to gag. I think, how amazing! I know he knew me that other time. But with Mama Charles here, suddenly I've got a name. I guess I didn't have one when I came in by myself. Now, he's falling all over himself to help this same little kid.

It isn't the only time I'm treated that way. Without Mama Charles, this 'uptown' experience, the one my friends warn me about, where people are rude, happens over and over. And it's not very subtle!

*

Thank goodness, my experiences in uptown Oxford aren't all like that. The place I really love to go is the Lane Public Library. It's tucked away in the corner of the main square about three doors down from that 'forbidden' Huddle restaurant. It's my safe place, the only place on High Street where I feel welcome. I can walk in by myself and nobody follows me around. The librarians ask if I need help, but that's what librarians do. Nobody's creeping me out.

Mrs. Tolka and Mrs. Stratten are the main librarians. Both are white women, but they accept all us kids, Colored, white, whatever. At school I keep winning the Governor's Ohio Reading Circle Award, so they know I like books. Most times they greet me with, "Ah ha, are you here to pick up more books Bernie? Did you enjoy such and such? Let me suggest this one." Thanks to them I gobble up book after book after book.

One day, I'm searching for a book to read. Mrs. Stratten, the head librarian, sees me. In her low library voice she says, "Bernie, you have read every book around you."

"Almost," I whisper. I'm concentrating on the bookshelf, seeing if I missed any gem. I'm not paying much attention to her. She continues talking.

"Well, what I am going to do, if the Charles will allow and you want to, is send you over to the campus library." Immediately, I am paying attention to her!

"The campus library?" I whisper loudly. "You—you mean the Miami University library?"

"Yes, Bernie," she says, nodding and smiling. "The university library. Want to? If your parents agree, I will call Mrs. Bell at the Miami library. I'm sure it can be arranged."

Mrs. Stratten's words shock me. "Yes Ma'am!" I squeal. Everybody in the library looks up, frowning at me. I just broke the 'quiet' rule. I cover my hot face with my hand, trying to hide my shock. Mrs. Stratten waves her hand at the room.

"It's okay," she says in her normal voice. Meanwhile, reality sets in. Back to whispering, I nervously ask, "Do—do you, do you think they will let a Col—"

"A girl your age in?" she interrupts. "I think so. Let's find out. I will call today. Then we'll see what your parents say."

Two days later I am standing on the front door steps of the Miami University library. The doors are huge. With two hands I pull one open and look inside. A white lady sees me, waves and walks over.

"Hello, Miss Bernie," she says warmly. "You are right on time. I'm Mrs. Bell. Let's go find some books for you."

For the next hour she shows me around the library. Each floor of this huge building is filled to the ceiling with rows and rows of books. Mrs. Bell calls them 'the stacks.' I guess it's because books are stacked on top of books on top of books. I figure there must be millions of books here. We walk back to the front checkout desk. That's when I get up my nerve to ask, "Can I read any book I want?" Mrs. Bell chuckles and says, "Yes, of course you may Bernie. Any book at all."

I have more questions. "What time do you close? Can I stay till closing or do I have to leave before then?" Mrs. Bell laughs again and says, "Well, the library closes really late, usually midnight, so I don't think that's possible. I talked to Mrs. Charles. Till you get older, you may stay until you get tired of reading or until 5 o'clock. That's when I get off work. I live on upper Oak Street, so I can walk you most of the way home."

Hot dog, I think. I'm in heaven. All those books, it's like they're saying to me, "Bernie pick me. Open me up, see what adventures we can have together." And that's exactly what I'm going to do.

I must say, those librarians, especially Mrs. Bell and Mrs. Stratten, but many others too, make me feel wonderful. Unlike the Mr. Cutlers of the world, they don't care about my skin color, age or whatever 'status things' get put on me. They just want this little girl, who has never been anywhere really, to visit the world and people in it through 'their' books. Being at their library, along with the books I read, makes me more confident about myself. For sure it helps me prepare for whatever is to come along. Best of all, it helps me put that 'Johnny thing,' that still nags at me, out of my mind. How lucky is that!

*

One day another 'book' lady comes into my life. The Charles and I are uptown doing what they call 'errands.' After returning a library book, I sit down on the curb in front of Minnis Drug Store to wait for them. A lot of white teenagers hang out at Minnis' soda fountain, laughing and talking as they sip cherry or vanilla cokes.

Eventually, Mr. Minnis tells them to buy something else or leave. I know, because I have white friends in there who tell me they are always getting chased out. Colored kids do the same thing at Knox's Grocery down on Sycamore Street. Our soda fountain is a tipsy wood picnic table outside the store where we sit and drink 'cold case' soda. It's that 'difference' again. But it's fun. And we get to hang outside Knox's as long as we want.

Anyway, while I'm waiting, a car pulls up to the curb on the other side of the alley and parks. I have never seen a car like it. I know it's not a Buick. Daddy Charles likes Buicks, so I know what they look like. This car is REALLY fancy. It looks like a chauffeur is driving, so it must be a rich man's car. But then I see a little white lady get out. She has what adults call 'purpose' to her. She wears a gray dress with gray stripes in it and a gray hat. She has on gray shoes. They have a small heel and white laces run up the front. And she carries a gray purse. It all looks like a uniform. No wonder I thought a chauffeur was driving.

As they say, 'curiosity got the cat' and that's me. I call out, "Lady, what kind of car is that?"

"It's a Cord. There aren't that many," she replies, looking my way with a small smile. That's it. She goes down the street and disappears into a ladies clothing store.

After that, I only see that lady from a distance, either driving that Cord car around uptown or parking at some curb. But one day, as I wait for Mama Charles, the Cord lady walks by me. She stops and says, "You like my car don't you?"

"Yes, Ma'am, I do."

We start to talk. For several minutes she quizzes me about life's little things, what I like and stuff like that.

"I like lots of things," I say. "Animals, birds and especially trees. I like to paint and play too. But I really love to read."

"You love to read?" she asks. Without hesitating, she goes on, "Would you like to read at my home? I have quite a library with lots of great books."

I'm stunned. I start wondering, what's up? A fancy white lady is inviting me to her home to read her books? Just like that? Why? Who is she? I mean, she's friendly but—

All I can do is stand there with nothing to say. That's not like me, but my mind is going a hundred miles an hour. Finally my curiosity gets me again.

"You have lots of books?"

"Yes, of course, I have plenty of books, of all kinds," she says. I'm in awe. She is full of confidence. But of course she is a white woman with fancy clothes and beautiful car so why wouldn't she be. Still—

Without waiting for me to agree, she goes on. "Okay then, let's arrange it. I will call Mrs. Charles and see what she thinks." Again I'm stunned. Somehow she knows Mama Charles. "O—okay," I say, trying to act calm. Inside I'm very excited, but also a little bit scared of her.

Two days later, the 'gray Cord' lady telephones Mama Charles. After talking it out, we all say 'yes' to her idea. The next day she picks me up in the Cord and drives me uptown to her home. I walk into the house. It's beautiful. It has a huge living room with big soft leather chairs. The rug is so thick that when I walk on it my feet sink way down and almost disappear from sight. Just like she said, her library room is full of books. They are lined up from floor to ceiling. Boy, I think, she has her own 'stacks.' I've never been inside or seen a house like this. She really is a 'book' lady.

I only go to the 'book' lady's house a couple of times. She's very nice and has lots of good books. But I like going to the library by myself whenever I want. Also, I love wandering through the university library, being around the college students, even pretending to be one. Most of all, I like getting lost in all those stacks and stacks of books. I mean, there aren't any cushy chairs or carpets to sink my feet into at the library, but it's more fun for a little kid. It feels safe, like being in a tree. I tell Mama Charles. She understands. I call the lady and thank her very much for her invitation. "You are welcome Bernie. It's been wonderful knowing you," she says.

Getting off the phone, I think about what she said about 'knowing' me. I realize I don't really know much about her. In fact she is a big mystery to me. I sure do appreciate what she did, though I still don't know why she picked me out. She never mentioned my reading awards. Maybe she saw something in me; some spark or maybe she felt sorry for me sitting alone outside of Minnis Drugstore. My guess is she knows something about me that I don't know. Maybe the librarians, most likely Mrs. Stratten, told her about me, about where I came from or what I went through. Wait, that can't be. I never told anybody, let alone white people, about any of that stuff. Whatever, she was nice to me. Because of her, I start looking at white people a little different.

1959. The Ohio Civil Rights Act of 1959 is passed to "prevent and eliminate the practice of discrimination in employment against persons because of their race, color, religion, national origin, or ancestry." In order to end segregation in restaurants, movie theaters, and other businesses, the act guarantees all people fair access to public facilities and private businesses. The Ohio Civil Rights Commission is created to enforce the law.

Chapter 9

Deep Thinking

Happy day! I'm starting Stewart Junior High School. Finally, I don't have to be in the same building with the little kids. And we don't stay in one room all day. That makes me feel really grown up. But from the first day of school, I come face to face with the really ugly side of racism. Some of it comes from very strange places. It makes me think a lot harder about people, white and Colored, in fact all kinds of people.

As usual, there aren't many Colored kids at school. Soon we start to hear 'the words' from some white students. Not so much from the Oxford kids, the ones we went to elementary school with, although it does happen with them a little too. It's the new kids bused in from small farm towns, mostly Summerville and Collinsville, outside of Oxford. I don't think these towns have many, if any Coloreds. Those kids don't know us, but they sure have plenty of names for us, like nigger, negroid, blackie, tar baby, darkie, coon, whatever. That's when the fights start. Call me Aunt Jemima or any of those names and I'll fight you! Me, Lulu Jones, Bobby Jackson, Roy Martin, a few others, stand up for ourselves, for us all really.

You'd think Colored folk would want us to fight back, but they don't. At school the Colored kids are really mixed up about how to deal with racist stuff. Is it better to play it down, pretend you don't hear it, pretend that you don't exist, a definite 'don't rock the boat' attitude? That's what most kids do or what their parents want them to do. Or should we have a certain mentality, proud of being Colored? If so, you don't let that stuff go, even if it rocks that old boat. If it's left to me, there's no choice. I'll fight it. I WILL rock that boat. It just seems right to want to be treated fairly. No more Johnnys in my life, whatever color.

But it's not just about me. It's about all of us; Mama and Daddy Charles, Walter, Belinda, my friends from Sycamore Street, Mrs. Stratten, the Gray 'book' lady, the white kids at Minnis Drugstore. I begin to think hard about all that stuff, trying to figure it out. It's all so new, yet already old. As usual, I have my questions. Where do I—we fit into all this? What is our place and what should it be? How do we get there? Should we get there?

At twelve years old, I do know one thing for sure. I'm tired of people telling me I can't do things or I have to do things their way. I mean, I already proved those doctors wrong about my body, at least part way. I'm strong and can run like the wind, faster than most kids my age. But all the nastiness, the pressure I put up with minute by minute when I leave the Charles house is confusing me. My mind's buzzing all the time. I need help, but I'm not getting much from adults, white or Colored. It seems most of them just want to ignore the racism, hoping it will go away if everybody just behaves and stays in their place. Even Mama Charles tells me, "Be calm Miss B."

*

Thank goodness, I'm getting to know Billie's father, Mr. Franklin Jacks. He has an upholstery shop out back of their house and an office inside, so he's around when we kids come over. All of us like to talk to him, especially me. I love to go out back and watch him smoking his pipe and working. He doesn't mind if I ask him questions. I don't really know what Mr. Jacks is doing in little ole' Oxford, he is so different from everybody. I ask Mama Charles about him. Frowning, she says, "That man is from Washington

D.C. He sees things differently from most of us. He's very militant, very sure about things."

It's true. Mr. Jacks doesn't pull any punches. Hard as it is sometimes, I like what he says, his message. Thanks to him, I start to look at the race thing differently, to think more about the equality thing and go after it with 'attitude.' He pushes all the time, telling me, "If you want it bad enough, you have to fight hard for it. If you want justice, you have to fight for it. If you want your right place in life, you have to fight for it. Nobody is going to give it to you. You have to go out there and let them know that it is your world too and that you have a place in it. You have a right to be here."

I love those words! I may be only twelve, but I already know I'm not the kind of person who is going to stand back and be quiet. Mr. Jacks likes my attitude. He also cares what I think, doesn't put me down just because I'm a young girl, a State kid. Like Mama and Daddy Charles, he's very proud, but a lot noisier about it than they or other Oxford Coloreds are. I guess that's what being militant is.

I'm also looking more at how others think of me. I begin to see that, well, I stick out like a sore thumb. I'm very different from other people. Even as a young kid, I'm more outgoing than most people. I'm not afraid to say what I feel, especially if people are telling me something that doesn't add up. I won't buy it. If your ideas or rules don't make sense, don't try to jam them down my throat. I will check things out on my own. If I get it, okay. If not, forget it. I mean, I want to get along but—.

I don't know where I get the feisty stuff. I remember what they said about Mama being a fighter before she got with Johnny. Maybe that's it. Still, it really makes me very different from my Colored and white friends. They seem confused, always hesitating. It's especially true of Colored kids. It's like they don't understand much of what's going on. Some do a little, like my girl friends who told me about the north side and 'difference' thing. But even they mostly won't stand up for themselves or others. Their attitude is 'just get by.' Also, there's a fear, it's like they don't want to stir things up. Most Oxford Coloreds, that's their way. It's like they've been beaten down already. And it seems half of them want to be white. Really! Many of the Colored kids want to be white or get along with whitey so much that they find ways to go after me. They say I'm too dark. They taunt me with, "Hey Shine! You so black, you must be straight out of some African jungle." Or, "Hey tar baby, ya goan out ta play wid yoo ape?" I get called 'ink spot' and 'chocolate girl' all the time. Of course, I mostly hear it from light skin Coloreds. I don't get it. It's like racism on top of racism.

I ask Mr. Jacks about it. He frowns and says, "It's hard, I know. But don't blame them too much. They don't know who they are or their own history yet. They'll find out soon enough one way or another."

Plenty of kids also go after me about being a State kid. I hear a lot of, "Hey Nigger, not only is you ugly, your mama dresses you funny. Oh, wait, you ain't got no mama."

Then there's how I talk. They say I sound like a whitey. I'm not sure about that. I hear lots of white folks messing up English. I just like to speak like people do in the books I read, especially use the cool words I find in history books. To me it's about learning new things.

All these things, my dark skin, the 'State kid,' the way I talk; a lot of the Colored kids cause me trouble. Not all of them, but many. So, I'm fighting that too. It's hard because a lot of times it's very subtle, like staring at me wanting to say, "Who are you? Don't you know how to act? Don't you know better?" But most times it's very obvious. I hang out down on the north side a lot, but many of the kids never invite me into their home. I'm not stupid. I get that message. And if there are white kids around who they're trying to be cool with, well guess who they go after? And it's not just me. They do the same to other kids, like Janet Nickerson and her brothers, who also get insults about being dark and poor. Most people don't know their dad is like Johnny, but I do. It's no wonder we are good friends.

All this 'difference' stuff really gets me, especially when it's coming from Coloreds. Mr. Jacks tries to help me with it, says folks don't get that whether we are black, brown or even 'yella,' to whitey we're all the same. But more and more it doesn't matter what folks do or say about me, I refuse to stay in my place like 'they' want me to. Call me militant if you want, I don't care. It's who I am.

1960, February 1. In Greensboro, North Carolina, four Negro college students refuse to leave a Woolworth's lunch counter until they are served. The 'Greensboro sit-in' starts an anti-segregation movement that quickly spreads to other college towns in the South.
1960, May 6. President Dwight D. Eisenhower signs the Civil Rights Act of 1960. In addition to protecting Negro citizens' voting rights, the law contains enforcement provisions against bombings and local interference with federal court orders. The legislation faced strong opposition from southern segregationists, sparking the longest filibuster in United States Senate history of 125 hours.

Chapter 10

Looking Through Stained Glass Windows

At the end of seventh grade, Becky Stevenson, one of my good friends, moves to Hillsboro Ohio, a town two hours from Oxford. That was almost a year ago and boy, I sure miss her. One day, Mama Charles says she has 'cake' business in Hillsboro and asks if I want to go visit Becky. "Oh yes!" I squeal in delight.

Mama Charles drops me off at Becky's house and goes about her business. After a little catching up, Becky and I decide to walk downtown. On the way, we pass a pretty little church with gorgeous stained glass windows. I have always loved colored glass windows. With the sun shining on them, they really sparkle. "Let's go see what the inside of that church looks like," I say. I tug at Becky's arm, but she pulls away.

"We can't go in there," she whispers.

"Why not?" I ask out loud.

"Cause Coloreds aren't allowed in there," she whispers again, her voice trembling.

That surprises me. I look straight at that little church. I'm wondering, what the heck is this? I've never paid much attention to churches, but as far as I know everybody chooses the one they like. After all, it's about God. What does he care? All of us Charles' kids go to the Elm Street Christian Church. But that's because we are with Mama and Daddy Charles. It's their church. If I want to go to any other church, I'm sure I can.

Again, I don't like people telling me I can't do something, especially if it's stupid. And not being allowed in this little church seems really stupid. I don't know, I guess I just like to torture myself. I frown at Becky and ask, "You're telling me just because we are Colored, we can't go in a church?" Becky nods and says, "This is Hillsboro. It's different from—"

"But all I want to do is go inside," I cut in. "I don't want to stay, just see the inside. Let's go knock on the door and ask if we can go in their nice little church."

Before Becky can say no, I shout, "Let's go!" I grab her arm and pull her up the steps. We trot around to the side door and knock. A chubby gray haired white lady opens the door. She stares at us, a scowl on her face. Becky tries to hide behind me.

"What do you want?" the lady demands. Mama Charles teaches us to always put our best foot forward, so I give the lady my biggest smile. Talking as fast as I can, I explain, "We would love to take a look at your church. It is so beautiful outside. It must be extra pretty inside. I am really interested in how things are made. Can we see the inside?"

The lady, hands on hips, just stares us down. Still, my fast talk seems to have got to her. With a big sigh, she turns and disappears into the dark building. A minute later she comes back with a bald, older white man. Maybe he's the preacher; I don't know for sure. He also frowns down at us.

"Can we come in?" I ask him politely. "We love your church and—"

"No," he interrupts. "Negros do not attend our church. So no, you can't come in."

Now I'm really confused and a bit frustrated. Then I remember something our preacher says. I look up at the churchman and blurt it out.

"We—we are all God's children. Why can't we see his church?"

The churchman stares down at me. I think something I said caught him off guard; surprised him. "Yes, b—but that—," he stammers.

Now I am getting upset. Plus, I can't help myself. It's just me. Before he can say no again, I pour it on.

"We are supposed to be able to go anywhere we want to worship him. Are you saying we, I can't come in because of the way I look? My color? I don't understand that. I don't think God would want that."

The churchman looks at the lady, then back at me. "What part did you want to see?" he demands. Now I am caught off guard. I really didn't expect him to give in so easily. I haven't thought about what I want to see. I just thought we would roam around inside. I don't think that's going to happen, so I make a quick decision. "I want to see your benches. Are your benches made of wood? I love wood ones. I want to see how they are made." He nods and growls, "The pews are wood. Come quickly."

I grab Becky's hand. The churchman leads us into a giant room with two rows of benches. Sure enough, they are made of shiny dark brown wood with pretty designs carved in them. Leaving Becky and the churchman, I walk up the aisle, gently touching each bench with my hand. They are silky smooth. I sit down in the front bench. It is hard but soft at the same time. I'm thinking the preacher better be good at preaching or people are going to nod off sitting here.

"That it?" the churchman yells from the back of the room. I'm already staring at the stained glass windows behind the altar. The sun shining through makes the blue and red colors sparkle even more than they do on the outside.

"Are there more colored windows to see?" I holler back.

"Come back here," he barks.

As our voices echo around the high walls, I trot back down the aisle and grab Becky's hand. It's shaking and sweaty. Dragging her along, we follow the churchman to the front entry room where there are two more stained glass windows. Becky fidgets nervously while I look at them closely. They are green and yellow with little red stars that twinkle in the sunlight.

"Okay, that's it," the churchman growls. He leads us back to the side door where the white lady still stands. She has a handkerchief in her hand, twisting it around and around her fingers. She's as nervous as Becky.

"Thank you very much," I say to the churchman. "You have a really beautiful church."

Out the side door we go. It clangs shut. I hear the lock 'click' behind us. I guess they don't want in any more of us coming around wanting to see inside their beautiful church.

Walking back to her house, Becky is still really scared. Looking around, she sputters, "Bernie they don't ever, never let us in that church! W—we don't even dare get close to it. There's gonna be hell to pay for somebody for sure!"

"Why do you say that?" I ask. She looks around nervously and says, "You live in Oxford. It's different over here."

On the way home I tell Mama Charles about my church adventure. She chuckles, shakes her head and says, "Okay, Miss Curiosity, tell me all about the beautiful inside of that church." I just talk and talk all the way home.

A few days later I share my adventure with Mr. Jacks. He tells me Becky is probably right about 'hell to pay' because the Ku Klux Klan is very active in lots of southern Ohio towns. He says in Lebanon, a town Mama Charles and I drove through on our way to Hillsboro, the Klan has rallies and cross burnings all the time.

I don't know what will happen to that pretty little church after my visit. With the Klan around, I doubt they will let Colored or Negros, as the churchman said, in. All I know is that on that one day, when a little girl said, "It's God's home. All God's children should be allowed to go in there," it put that churchman on the spot. And I did go in there!

1961, May 6. Thirteen (seven Black and six white) men and women civil rights activists, sponsored by the Congress For Racial Equality, leave Washington D.C on the first of many Freedom Rides. Traveling by bus, they cross interstate lines and attempt to integrate 'whites only' restrooms and lunch counters along the way to New Orleans. They are met with violence from white protesters, including the burning of their Greyhound bus in Anniston Alabama.

Chapter 11

Lessons From A High School Yearbook

It's Fall, 1960, and I'm going to Talawanda High School. I am so excited. I mean, high school! Everybody seems so grown up, especially the juniors and seniors. I think, finally all that old crap, stuff that kids do about being Colored or white, rich or poor, girl or boy, even that 'State kid' stuff will go away. Now it's about Talawanda pride, everybody pulling together.

For a while it sure seems that way. The first week Principal Baker warns that racism is not tolerated at Talawanda. During school hours, Coloreds and whites mix in the hallways and sit next to each other in classrooms. Some even share hall lockers. I know Bobo Grosscup and Ronnie Martin do. Nancy Franklin and Frieda Smith do too.

I don't mean all the obvious stuff is gone. Talawanda is a new unified high school, so there are even more kids from towns that aren't used to Coloreds. There are also the supposedly 'hotshots' from Miami's all-white McGuffey school. So we still hear 'the words' sometimes, but nothing like Junior High. Most racist stuff gets dealt with off campus after school or at night. Living on the south side with the Charles, I'm lucky not to be involved in any of that. Lucky so far, that is. Of course I hear about the fights that happen a few blocks from the high school, uptown or on the walk over to the north side. When Colored and white kids come to school with black eyes, messed up noses and patched clothes, it's pretty clear what's going on.

Still, I'm excited to be in high school. But soon the subtle racism, the kind that doctors claim gives Colored people high blood pressure, hits me. After a couple of months at Talawanda, Mama Charles checks my blood pressure. It's up some.

My first experience with Talawanda's 'subtle' racism happens after the first home football game. Our Talawanda Braves, we have Colored and white players, beat one of the teams from the Cincinnati area. Everybody cheers them on, everyone, together.

After the game, there is a 'sock hop' in the school gym. I walk in with some of my 'sisters.' Right away I see a big crowd of white students laughing and talking loud on the near side of the gym. A few girls are dancing in their socks to the rock music blasting from the loudspeaker. The older boys, mostly athletes and their friends, stand around with their shoes on, too cool to dance for sure. The freshman boys are running around in their socks, playing tag, yelling at each other and laughing. I see my neighbor Henry, the booger eater, sneaking through the crowd pulling guys' shirt tails out, then running off. Walking along, my friend Linda, a junior, says. "Come on Bernie, we're over there." I look where she is pointing. Over in the far corner of the gym, all the Colored kids, including the football players who had just helped win the game, are standing together. We start to walk over when I see Bobo Grosscup bopping around like a fool with a girl I know he likes. Seeing me, he waves. I decide to kid him about how he's shaking his tail feather. I guess it's some sort of dance. Before I can do or say anything, Linda grabs my arm and says, "Bernie, we are over here!"

Pulling me along, we join the Colored kids. They're talking quietly among themselves. A few are swaying back and forth and snapping their fingers to the music. Nobody's acting like a fool, not even Robby Carter, who usually 'plays the clown.' I look back at the rowdy white crowd. I think, what a difference. I wonder why?

I ask Linda, "What's going on? Why are we all way over here? Why are we being so quiet?" Linda scowls and spits it out.

"It's the custom. Whites get to act like they want to, get to be loud and run around. We have to be on guard. If we laugh or talk loud, the word gets to us that we are 'uncouth.' If we dance too fast or you know, too raunchy, we are 'acting out of place,' showing that we really are jungle bunnies. Nobody says so directly. It's just understood. It's knowing your place, knowing the custom."

Confused, I let it go. At the next sock hop the same thing happens so I start asking other kids if Linda is right about the so-called custom. All the juniors and seniors say, "It's the way it is—don't fight it." Well, I don't like that! But being new at the school, I hold my tongue; back off for now.

Over my freshman year, even though I'm running track and very active, my blood pressure keeps going up little by little.

*

In my sophomore year, I start to really pick up on things; start to notice how whites are everywhere, but Coloreds are mostly nowhere. When I deal with faculty and administrators, except for Mrs. Drassy, who teaches business classes, they are all white. Even the cafeteria staff is all white women. Oh, excuse me; three of the four night janitors are Colored. Hooray!

At our sports events, all the cheerleaders and band drum majorettes are white. The same is true at social events. The homecoming and prom king and queen and their courts are all white. Of course that makes some sense. If a Colored dares to run, they won't get elected. There just aren't enough of us. At least that what's I thought—then surprise! Michael Mathis, a popular, good looking Colored athlete, and good student, is elected Homecoming King. Nobody, and I mean n-o-b-o-d-y can believe it! Me either. A few whites say it shows how far Oxford has come on civil rights. But I hear about a lot of others telling their friends, "No way did I vote for that nigger king." How did it happen? A lot of people say someone stuffed the ballot box. That's what most of the bigots think. My sources say they're right about that.

There's a real racial split in Talawanda sports. Colored boys are 'encouraged' to go out for basketball, track, football and baseball. Supposedly they're 'our' sports. None of us are on the boys' golf and tennis teams or girls' field hockey and volleyball teams. Except for my friend Janet Nickerson, the girls' varsity and reserve basketball teams are white. Except for me, the girls' track team is white and it isn't even an official sport. We race ourselves. I'm faster than all those white girls, except Bobo's sister.

In the outside world, Coloreds are very into music, but not at Talawanda. When our orchestra performs at school, I notice that except for one drummer, the musicians are white. Two of us are in the marching and concert bands. The school choir is pretty integrated, but that's because the new director really goes after boys of whatever color to join. Some colored boys are members of The Neutrals, an a cappella group. Sometimes they sing at the sock hops. That's our place. We are the high school's runners and jumpers and sock hop entertainers; the boys are that is. Girls, even tomboys like me, are 'just girls.'

For me, something worse is going on. Every time I sign up for classes, the counselors are very strict about what classes I should take or not take. When I ask my friend Johanna, a senior about it, she gets right to it. "Girl, it's racism. The faculty tell us we won't make it in some classes, so don't even try." I don't want to believe her. I hope the counselors are just trying to help us get through high school.

Well of course I ask Mr. Jacks about all this. He frowns, takes a puff on his pipe and says, "Bring your high school yearbook to me." When I do, he flips to the Academic Club pictures and shows me the effect of our 'counseling.' The Latin and French clubs are all white. The Spanish club has one Colored out of twenty-two members. The Theater Club and Science Club are white, so are the yearbook and student newspaper staff. The forty-three member National Honor Society has one Colored boy. The pictures also show it's rare for one of us to be a student leader. That year, two guys, Harry Kanes and Dale Simpson, are elected President and

Vice President of their classes. That's great! But the all-school Student Council is completely white.

"Maybe it's our fault," I say to Mr. Jacks. "Nobody is stopping us from taking those classes and joining clubs or running for office."

"That's right," he says, smiling at me. "We should. So why don't we—you do it? What's stopping you?" Without saying anything more, I realize Mr. Jacks is pushing me to act, to be different, but letting me know there are some hurdles to get over.

Back home, I study the yearbook pictures over and over, seeing them in a different light. I think about my senior friends who told me the Talawanda academic advisors never talk to even the best Colored students about their college plans. Well, the whole school knows I'm bent on going to college, so I didn't believe them. But now, it makes sense. Even though Miami University is just up the street from where we live, those counselors think college is 'out of reach' for us. But it's not walking distance we are talking about. They mean college is intellectually out of reach for us.

Bobo Grosscup is a graduating senior, so I talk to him about this. He says the counselors have never spoken to him about college either.

"B—but you're white and your dad's a professor," I sputter.

"I know," he replies. "But I went to Stewart school, so the counselors assume I'm not going to college. My sister went to McGuffey. As a junior she was counseled about colleges and took all the tests her senior year. My parents say it's the McGuffey school snob thing going on. Go to McGuffey? Of course we'll talk you about college. If not, then forget it. But I'm not going to college right away, so it doesn't matter much to me."

Well, it matters to me! I talk to Mama Charles. She says, thanks to the local NAACP, last year Miami University dropped the 'administrative barriers' that kept us out of McGuffey. So far no Colored children have enrolled. I bet the "you are not welcome, what are you doing here" situation is going on there too; keeping us out.

There are also some outstanding Colored athletes at Talawanda, but nobody counsels them about a college athletic scholarship either. As a sophomore, even with my nasty burn scars I can outrun everybody on the girls varsity track team. Anyone talk to me about a scholarship? No. I know two white boys who can't read a lick, but ended up with athletic scholarships. They got 'counseled' for sure.

I get what Mr. Jacks wanted me to 'see' in that high school yearbook. At Talawanda the subtle message to Coloreds is, your place in life is set. Don't think beyond it. Above all else, don't rock that boat.

I'm halfway through my sophomore year and getting fed up with what's going on. I'm getting good grades, and I love school, especially reading and science discovery parts. But the more I know about the limits they try to place on me, on us, the more I don't like it. I want to be as great as I can be. So, starting now, over the last two years of high school I'll make sure they pay attention to at least one Colored girl. No more of this 'be twice as good and get half as much' stuff.

But now, Sammy is my life.

1961, March. Elmer and Carmel Whiting integrate Shaker Heights Ohio. Their son, Jerry, becomes the first Black student at Onaway Elementary School.

1961. Ohio's Laws Against Discrimination is amended to include the prohibiting of employment discrimination.

Chapter 12

Sammy

Lunch hour is almost over. I'm on my way from the outside eating area into the school building and math class when I hear, "Hey girl. Come sit by me."

I look over to see a brown boy sitting on a bench, patting a place beside him. I sort of know him, or rather know about him. He's Sammy Collins. His grandma lives three houses up from the Charles. All the girls are crazy about him. He's nice looking, though skinny and a bit short. He's in the Neutrals, so I guess he can sing. I hear he is a pretty good athlete, fast like me, although I never see him on any high school teams. He has a rep for getting in trouble, for skipping school, being what we call a 'wile child.' Coaches don't put up with that stuff from a Colored kid.

Sammy has that 'something,' that underdog trait, same as me. I think that's what draws me to him now. I take the plunge, walk over and sit down on the other end of the bench. "I'm Sammy," he says, moving to the middle of the bench. "I see you around. People say things about you. You're Bernie, right?"

"Yes," I say, surprised that anyone talks to him about me. "I know you, I mean I know your grandmother, Miss Nell. She lives up the street from us." Frowning, he replies, "Oh yeah, you live on the south side close to the Nell family. You live with the Charles, girl? You one of those State kids?"

"Yes, but the Charles are my family, not the State," I shoot back. My confident tone catches him off guard. He frowns, waves a 'no matter' hand and says, "Okay girl, if you say so. But I live with my real family, my dad at least. We live on the north side. That's where most of us are except the Charles, Miss Nell and a few others, and you." He hesitates, then mutters, "And my mama. She lives with Gramma Nell. Don't ask me why."

I'm surprised. I have seen a pretty woman walking out of Miss Nell's house several times. I just thought she was visiting. "Your mama lives with Miss Nell?" I ask. "Why?"

"I told you don't ask me!" he snaps. Anger fills his face, but quickly disappears.

"Parents: they don't get along, fight a lot," Sammy mumbles. He looks off, then back at me, smiling. "Aaah," he says, "It's nothing. It's better she's over at Gramma Nell's." Looking me over, he says, "Girl you sure looking fine. Getting all grown up now. I hear you're fast. Got those running legs for sure."

It's true. My body is really changing. Last week Mama Charles measured me at five feet two inches tall. My legs and arms are nothing but muscles. And I am filling out in the hips and booty, you know, where it matters. My breasts are growing too. I don't want really big breasts. They may cut down my running speed. May even mess with my burned belly. My face is losing that little girl look too. I still have my toothy smile and big bright eyes, but Mama's high cheekbones are showing. A friend of Mama Charles says I look like some ancient Egyptian queen called Nefertiti. Of course I looked her up at the library. She was beautiful and smart!

"Yes, I'm pretty fast," I reply. "I win—"

Standing up, he interrupts me, "Fast for a girl that is, 'cause you can't beat me. But that doesn't matter. Just the way it is. Say, whatcha doing right now?" Before I can answer, he grabs my hand and pulls me to my feet. "Come on, let's go," he says. It's almost an order. The class bell rings.

"Where are you going?" I ask. "You're not going back to class?"

"Naw, I'm skipping," Sammy says, looking around for the school monitor. "Nothing here for me. I'm going uptown. I got a job helping Lonnie Mack set up his drums and guitar. He's playing every Wednesday at the CI." Puffing out his chest, he goes on. "Lonnie says if I help him, I can stand at the door and listen as long as I want. He plays past midnight; says if I'm still there I get extra for helping pack up stuff. I'm staying for sure."

I look around. Everyone is headed into the school building except Sammy and me. The late bell is going to ring soon. "Come on little mama," he says. "There's nothing in school for a State kid. You can help me set up the drums. Later tonight we can meet uptown and go listen to Lonnie. He pla—"

"I told you, I'm not a State kid," I quickly cut in. "Besides, I like school. And if we get caught, Mama Charles, she'd be upset. She expects me to be in school."

"If you get caught," he laughs. "Okay girl, you stay in school. But just so you know. Nobody is gonna catch you if you're with me."

Sammy turns to go. Throwing me a wink over his shoulder, he jogs off. I watch him go up the street and disappear. As I head into the school building, the late bell sounds. "Damn, I'm late," I mumble. But I don't really care. I'm floating on air after talking to Sammy. Despite his 'State kid' stuff, I like him, am drawn to him. He seems so carefree and worldly, especially next to me. I can't wait to see him again. I know he's what they call 'forbidden fruit.' Maybe that's what attracts me. I've had fruit before, but not that kind.

*

Several weeks later, I'm in the kitchen washing the supper dishes. Belinda has finished clearing the table and gone upstairs. I hear the front door open. I walk over to the kitchen door and peek around the corner. I see Mama Charles and a tall thin man standing in the front hallway. He sticks out his hand and says, "Good evening Mrs. Charles. I am John Collins. Miss Nell is my mother."

I hear the name Collins. I think, bet he's Sammy's dad.

"Yes, I recognize you, Mr. Collins. Your mother speaks highly of you," Mama Charles says, shaking his hand. Her words are polite, but I know from her tone that she isn't excited to see him at our house.

"And she of you, Mrs. Charles," he replies. "And Mr. Charles too of course."

"What can I do for you Mr. Collins?" Mama Charles asks in her formal voice. I can tell she wants a short visit.

"Mrs. Charles," he says. "I was wondering. I—we've got, that is my wife and me, I believe you know my wife Ruby. She lives with my mother. We're divorced as you probably heard—"

"Yes, I know Ruby Collins," Mama Charles says, interrupting him. "As to your situation, I make it my business not to pry."

"I appreciate that," Mr. Collins replies. "So many folks are—"

"Mr. Collins, what can I do for you?" Mama Charles cuts in again. She is trying to be polite, but I can tell she is getting impatient. Nervously, Mr. Collins starts to explain.

"Mrs. Charles, as I was saying, we've—well really me, I've got two boys who live with me across town. And well, while I mean, I really, what with work and I, well—"

Mama Charles breaks in again. "Please, Mr. Collins. What about your boys? What are you trying to say?"

Mr. Collins' voice suddenly gets louder, booming down the hallway. "I was thinking they could come and live with you and Mr. Charles. They are, I mean, I can't take care of them. They are always in trouble, especially Sammy the oldest. He's, they aren't bad boys. They just get in a little trouble and I can't do much about it, you know what with working and all, and their mother being over here on the south side. I thought if you took them in for a spell that you and her and Mr. Charles of cour—"

Mama Charles cuts him short. "I'm sorry, Mr. Collins, we don't have room for them. Mr. Charles and I are doing all we can with the family we have. Now if you don't mind, I've got things to do."

Heading back to the sink, I hear the front door close. Mama Charles comes into the kitchen. She looks uptight. Seeing me, she asks, "Bernie, did you hear? Did you hear what that man wanted?"

"Yes, Ma'am. I tried not to, but he was really loud."

"I know he was. That man, he thinks we take in bad kids!"

Now Mama Charles' eyes stare right through me. I can tell she is choosing her words carefully. Finally she asks, "Bernie, do we take in bad kids?"

"No Ma'am," I answer quickly. "I don't—"

Mama Charles cuts me off. "Damn right we don't! We are not a home for bad kids. We—we take good kids, and love them and with God's help, teach them manners, and respect for themselves and others." Her voice goes up another notch. "And this surely isn't a house for parents to dump their kids for us to raise just because they can't or won't!"

I don't know what to say. I've never heard Mama Charles say 'damn.' Usually it's 'darn' or 'shoot.' Silently I watch Mama Charles fret. Seconds pass. Then, shaking her head, she walks over and starts rubbing my stack of clean pots dry. It's more like she is polishing them. After a while she looks up, sighs and says, "Oh, you're still here. What is it you were trying to say back awhile Bernie?"

"I—I was wondering. Why would anyone want to give up kids? I mean; I just don't get it. Kids need to be with their mama and dad. Mr. Collins needs to be with his boys. And, I don't know why he says Sammy is bad. I—"

Frowning at me, Mama Charles interrupts, "Do you know Sammy Collins?"

By this time, Sammy and I have been sneaking around for almost two months. We hang out after school and a little on weekends. He watches me run track and I go hear his Neutrals singing practice. Besides my brothers and sisters, he is my favorite person to be with. But of course, being with him is different. I love them, but I am 'in love' with him and he with me. At least that's what we sort of tell each other.

Talking quickly, I say, "I know him from school. He's one of the most popular kids. I don't know why Mr. Collins says he's bad. I've never seen him do anything to anybody. He's always nice to me. He's very polite, like you and Daddy want us to be."

"I see," Mama Charles mutters. "But just how well do you know him Miss B?"

I know what she's asking. Mama Charles is not stupid.

"He's just another one of my friends," I lie, trying to calm her.

"You know he's Miss Nell's grandson," she says, looking down at me. "I suspect Miss Nell and Mr. Collins know more than you about that rascal. From what Miss Nell says, he's starting out on the wrong side of things."

I look at Mama Charles. I don't know what to say back. I mean, I want to say that parents, adults don't know everything, but I don't. Not this time. Mama Charles reaches, grabs my hand and says, "I think it's best if you stay away from him Miss B."

Her words make my heart sink. Looking away from her I think, I love you Mama Charles and will do anything for you. But about Sammy, you are wrong, everybody is wrong and I can prove it. I just have to find a way. Then it hits me. I look at Mama Charles and say, "Mr. Collins and Miss Nell tell you Sammy is a bad boy, right?" Mama Charles nods in agreement. I go on.

"Still, Mr. Collins and maybe Miss Nell think it's a good idea if he and his brother come to live with us. I mean, Mr. Collins must think so much of you and Daddy Charles and how you can help folks out as to do something so awful as to give them up."

"Maybe," Mama Charles mutters. I think she's somewhat flattered by the compliment. She likes folks to think well of her.

"But we're not in the business of taking in bad kids," she says firmly. "I told him that already."

"Yes, I know. But Sammy doesn't have to live here. He—he could visit me, I mean us. That way you will get to know him to see if he really is what they say, you know, a bad boy. If he needs help staying out of trouble; if he hangs out here we can help him do it." A slight frown creeps over Mama Charles' face. I think I've got her where I want, so I keep talking fast. "We can invite him over some day, maybe tomorrow. He can watch American Bandstand with us. I think Sam Cooke is supposed to be on tomorrow."

Mama Charles looks me straight in the eyes. "No," she says.

"No? Why not?" I ask. A bit surprised by me being so pushy, Mama Charles quickly says, "Because, it's not his behavior I am or want to be responsible for. Not my business. MY business, Miss B, is you and your behavior, and the others. That is my concern right now, tomorrow, and everyday from here on out as long as you all are in this house. You understand that don't you?" Fixing my eyes on the floor, I mutter, "Yes Ma'am."

I can see Mama Charles' mind is set. But I'm not giving up. Twice more in the next month I ask her if Sammy can come to our house, once for dinner, the other just to sit on the porch with the family. A quiet but firm, "No" is all she says.

*

No matter what Mama Charles says, I am determined more than ever to see Sammy, my 'forbidden fruit.' I love Mama Charles and don't like going behind her back, but, well, what she doesn't know—. So Sammy and I sneak away every chance there is.

The time with my 'wild chile' Sammy is more fun than ever! We talk and laugh. Down on the north side, we boogie in friends' living rooms to fresh R&B, especially Claudine Clark's *Party Lights* and The Orions' *Wah-Watusi.* My favorite is The Crystals' *He's a Rebel.* I close my eyes and picture my rebel Sammy.

When Spring comes we run races across the fresh mowed fields of the Miami campus. Holding hands has led to a peck on the cheek, then a real 'Hollywood' kiss. It's all so fun, so exciting! In three months, school will be over and the summer will give us even more time together. I can't wait to hang out at the Bluffs with Sammy, show him my secret spots.

*

With school, running track, Sammy and lots of friends, my life is really full and moving fast. At barely fifteen, my body keeps changing too. My girlfriends kid about my breasts, telling me, "Girl, your boobs are more than a handful, they are ample." I catch the boys staring at them. My sister Janet helps me with what she calls my 'period.' I don't understand much about it and no one is about to explain it to me either. It seems for adults, 'body talk' is forbidden, you know, taboo. All I know is that, except for missing and wondering about my Walter, I am the happiest I can ever remember. I am growing up, learning lots of new things and loving it. But for some reason, Mama Charles isn't very happy right now.

1961, February 2. In Dayton Ohio, W.S. McIntosh leads Black civil rights activists carrying signs reading "Why Buy Where You Can't Work?" to protest hiring discrimination at white banks and businesses.

Chapter 13

Going Too Fast

I excuse myself from the dinner table and go upstairs to lie down on my bed. I'm swallowing a lot of spit, like I'm about to throw up. I love greens, but when Mama Charles set some in front of me at the dinner table, I almost got sick from the smell. It's the same thing I get from anything covered in white sauce. I'm a big eater and gulp down almost anything. Just don't put that white sauce on stuff that you want me to eat. But greens are my favorite, at least until now.

"Bernie," Mama Charles says entering my room. She's carrying a bowl of greens. Her eyes are filled with a sadness I remember seeing in my mama's eyes years ago.

"Where is your appetite tonight? You love greens."

"I know," I groan. "I do love them, but tonight they just don't smell right."

"Maybe those were spoiled," she says. "I brought some fresh ones from the kitchen." I sit up, take the bowl from her and put it to my nose. "Aaggggg!" I howl. Spit rushes to the top of my tongue. "They stink too!" I shoot up from the bed and sprint to the bathroom. I get on my knees and throw up into the toilet. A minute later, Mama Charles is standing at the bathroom door. "You finished?" she asks softly. "Yes Ma'am, I think so," I say, not really sure. I'm still spitting food pieces into the toilet. Finally, I get up and reach for my water glass and toothbrush. Mama Charles comes into the bathroom; shakes her head and starts to clean my lips with a washcloth. Tears are dripping from her eyes. "Oh, my little girl," she murmurs, shaking her head at me. "You were the belle—the belle of the ball." Her words confuse me, but I am too sick to talk. Mama Charles grabs me and for half a minute squeezes me tighter than she ever has. Letting go, she takes my hand, leads me to my bedroom and helps me into bed.

"Do you know what is wrong with you?" she asks quietly, a worried look on her face. I push the words out, "No, I don't. I—"

"I think you're pregnant," Mama Charles interrupts. Sadness chokes her voice.

"Mama Charles, I'm not pregnant!" I yell, bolting up in bed. I stare into her wet eyes. I can tell she is not convinced. "Yes B. I am sure you are pregnant," she says quietly but more firmly. "But no matter, we are going to see Dr. Reichart tomorrow."

"What? Dr. Reichart? Why? I can't be pregnant," I shout back. "I—you—you don't know anything. Nothing!" Vomit bubbles up my throat again. I jump out of bed. Rushing into the bathroom, I slam the door in Mama Charles's face and scream, "YOU KNOW NOTHING! I AM NOT PREG-AAAGG!" Vomit fills my mouth, drowning out that awful word.

The next day, we go to see Dr. Reichart. He examines every inch of my body, including 'down there' and gives me a pregnancy test.

*

A week later we return. Mama Charles is right. The tests say that I am pregnant, but according to Dr. Reichart, not in the 'normal' way. "Her hymen isn't broken," he says, turning to Mama Charles. "It must have stretched on the side, just a little bit. In a month or so, we will have to break it."

I am confused and getting upset. They are talking about me—my body being pregnant as though I'm not in the room. That's what the doctors tried to do at Mercy Hospital when I was burned.

Mama Charles knows that. And now they're talking about breaking something inside me; a hy-man or hy-men, whatever that is.

"How can I be pregnant?" I yell. "We—we had a hard time. I mean it didn't go in very far and it was only one time."

Mama Charles glares at me. Her frown tells me she doesn't like me interrupting adults. Dr. Reichart has a small smile on his face. "I know," he says, "I can tell, but sometimes all it takes is one little bugaboo to sneak around the side." Taking my hand he says, "For what it's worth young lady, it happens more than most folks know."

"Come now Bernice," Mama Charles says, nodding to Dr. Reichart. "Let's not take up anymore of Dr. Reichart's time."

"Wait!" I yell. "What does that mean; a bugaboo sneaking around? I—I want to—I—I don't know anything. What's a bugaboo anyway? I need—I want to know how the baby is going to get out of me. The burn doctors said I couldn't have a baby. So how the hell—"

Scared, I stop yelling and start to tear up. My belly scars are tingling. Mama Charles and Dr. Reichart glance at each other. Mama Charles nods to him. Dr. Reichart looks down at me and says, "Mrs. Charles will talk to you about all that Bernie, about all the changes that you will go through. They will be wonderful changes both inside and outside of your body. There is no reason to be afraid. You will know everything when it is time. And you can ask me anything, anytime."

His words don't help. I scowl at him and let him have it. "But Mama Charles—she never had a baby, so how's she going to help me? And she's never been burned up like I am either. What does she know? Nothing!"

My rant over, I shut up and look at Mama Charles. Her eyes are burning right through me. I know I really hurt her feelings. I didn't mean to, but—.

Dr. Reichart looks down at me, smiles and says, "Because, as you well know young lady, Mrs. Charles is a remarkable woman. You are so very lucky to have her in your life, especially now."

"Thank you Dr. Reichart," Mama Charles says, grabbing my hand and guiding me toward the door. "We will do our very best."

Driving home, Mama Charles talks about everything under the sun; from how late the tomatoes are to what a good bridge player Sheila Jackson is. Everything except what's making my head about to explode. As we turn onto Oak Street, I can't hold back. "Mama Charles, what things are going to happen to me that Dr. Reichart wouldn't say?" Without answering, Mama Charles stops the car in front of the house. She stares straight into the windshield for what seems like forever. Finally, looking over at me, she snaps.

"Miss Bernice, don't be in such a rush to know everything all the time!" Then, staring out of the windshield again, she mutters, "There's already been too much rushing around as it is."

It's the only time since knowing her that Mama Charles can't hide her disappointment in me.

*

Mama and Daddy Charles decide they will tell Sammy's parents and grandparents the news. Telling Sammy is my job. It goes okay. There is no denying and no blaming me. I still really like him, still feel he is a good person. But deep down, I also feel that this is probably the first time in his life Sammy has to do anything important. I mean, he's never had to look after anyone but himself.

"I will take care of you," is all he says. I don't know how he is going to do that being only seventeen and me just turned fifteen.

The adults decide that I am going to have the baby. I mean, what choice is there? I've heard about abortion, but nobody ever talks about it. I know it's illegal and I guess the Bible is against it. The only question is; am I going to keep the baby or give it up for adoption? But again, that isn't up to me. Mama Charles tells me straight out that I will raise that baby with or without Sammy. "It's not for you to decide Bernie. Kids need their parents and parents need their kids, even when it's babies having babies. I talked to your mother and she agrees. So that's that."

Talawanda High School, Oxford Ohio, circa 1957.

Chapter 14

The Worst News Ever

After the doctor visit, I start feeling good again as long as I stay away from certain foods. I pretty much go on with my life of going to school, doing homework and helping Mama Charles around the house. I hardly see Sammy. He drops out of school and has a part-time job on weekends, so there's not much chance of meeting up. I'm still training with the girls' track team, running close to my best times. I almost forget something is supposedly growing inside of me. Being pregnant, if I am, doesn't seem that hard. Maybe a mistake has been made after all.

Then one day, I am called to the Talawanda principal's office. I know Principal Baker a little. He's a kind man with twinkly blue eyes, the sort of eyes that say, "I'm seeing you." As principal, he goes out of his way to make Colored kids feel welcome at his school. For some reason, Mr. Baker seems to really like me. He often stops me in the hallway to ask me how school is going. Sometimes he calls me 'Kitten.'

I enter his office. Mr. Baker looks up and motions for me to sit down in the chair at the front of his desk. I look across at him. His usual smile is gone. In a serious voice, he gets right to it. "Bernice, there is a rumor going around about you."

"Wha—what k—kind of rumor?" I stammer. Mr. Baker leans forward in his chair, puts his elbows on the desk, and clenches his hands under his chin. His blue eyes stare straight at me. There's no twinkle today. "That you are pregnant," he says softly.

Pregnant! That word again. Now rumors about me being pregnant. When he says it, my stomach drops deep into my thighs. I start to sway back and forth. My heart feels like it's breaking into a million pieces. It's as though suddenly all of it is catching up with me. I feel so alone, so ashamed. I start to sob. Mr. Baker hands me a box of tissues from his desk. I pull a handful out and press them to my wet, hot face.

"Is it true?" he asks.

"Y—y—yes," I stutter between my sobs. Gulping down some air, I try again.

"I mean, yes, I—they say—I guess it is t—true. I'm so sorry Mr. Baker."

"I see," he replies. He looks down at his desk and pauses. Then, lifting his eyes he looks straight at me and says, "Bernice, you know you will have to leave school, don't you?"

His tone is very matter of fact. The words 'leave school' stun me. I never dreamed I couldn't go on as usual. At least up until the day I go to the hospital to have that baby. It never dawned on me that what's growing inside me wouldn't allow me to—. I look away from him, wipe my lips dry with the back of my hand and think, wow girl, you really messed up.

Quickly, my brain gets back on track. I think, wait a minute, leave school? Why? I'm running track, got really good times. I go to every class and study just like always. And until now, nobody at school really knew I'm pregnant. Sure, there might be rumors going round. I know that. People, kids talk. But hey, I'm not really sure if I am pregnant. Doctors make mistakes too. Still, the man across from me is telling me something I never thought would ever happen. I'm confused, don't like it. I need to tell him so.

"What do you mean, I can't stay in school? Mr. Baker you—you know how much my education means to me. I love school. We—you and I talk about it." Mr. Baker's voice turns even more serious. "Yes, but you're going to have to drop out. They won't let you stay if you are pregnant. And you just said you are, so—"

My whole body filling with anger, I cut him off. "Nobody ever said anything about having to drop out of school. Why don't you tell us these things? I would never have—"

I catch myself. What I'm about to say, I don't know if it's true or not. Sammy and I, what we did wasn't planned. It was all just playing at stuff, messing around, puppy love. Now things are changing for real. But I'm not going to give up school without a fight. I start in on Mr. Baker.

"What I mean is, it is true there are rumors about me being pregnant. But I don't really know if I am. I mean I don't feel like I am pregnant, so maybe I'm not."

Mr. Baker's blue eyes turn sad. He reaches for a folder on his desk. In a voice full of kindness, he says, "Kitten, I know you will do anything to be in school and I know you are confused by all that is going on. But according to this report from Dr. Reichart, there is no doubt."

Tapping his finger on the folder, Mr. Baker goes on. "When I hear a rumor, especially one like this, I check it out. You have been to the doctor, so you know regardless of how you feel, that it is true. I take his word and Mrs. Charles too, and now I have to take yours. I wish it were different, but I'm afraid you are going to have to drop—"

I start to bawl, drowning him out. I can't help it. I am swimming in tears and sadness. The box of tissues is empty. Mr. Baker leans over and hands me his handkerchief. Softening his voice, he says, "I'm sorry, Kitten, but there is nothing I can do. The Board has rules that I, everyone, and therefore you, have to follow."

"But what about graduation," I ask between sobs. "Does this mean just because I'm pregnant I can't graduate? That's not right, Mr. Baker. I—you know I want to go to college. I have to finish high school!"

Mr. Baker leans back in his chair, his hand on his chin. For a time he is quiet. Then he says, "Okay, let's think about this." He pauses again. Then, leaning towards me, in his 'principal's voice' he says, "Bernice, you go have that baby. And when you are ready to come back to school, you come and finish your education."

I listen to his words. Some of them, especially "go have that baby," I don't like. But when he says, "Finish your education," well, it's like he has thrown me a life raft. I am no longer drowning. "R—really?" I stammer. "Do y—you mean it? Will they let me do that? The Board? Are you sure, Mr. Baker?"

"I'm sure," he replies. "In fact, I promise. When you are ready, you come back, work hard and graduate."

I can't help it. I jump up, run around the desk and before he can get up, I hug him with all my might. "It's okay," he whispers, patting me on the back again and again. "We can do this. We can get you through." Letting him go, I shout, "Thank you, thank you, thank you!"

Quickly, I cover my mouth with my hand; afraid the people in the outer office can hear me. I still can't hide my smile, my joy. Mr. Baker smiles back at me, then he gets serious again.

"Okay Bernice, for now you may stay in school as long as you can. But remember, when the time comes, the Board is going to insist that you leave. You must go then—no ifs—no buts— no questions asked. No fuss. Do you agree?"

"I know, and I will do that. But maybe, Mr. Baker, it will turn out that I am not—" I lower my voice. "You know, pregnant. Then I wouldn't ha—"

Mr. Baker holds up his hand to stop me and says, "Bernice, when the time comes, you go have that baby and then come back."

"I still don't want to hear that," I mumble. Mr. Baker frowns at me. "Okay," I say. "I will do that. And you PROMISE I can come back, right?"

Mr. Baker smiles and says, "Yes Bernice, I promise. Now go to class."

I leave the principal's office and head off to English class. My head and heart are aching from the worst news ever. But Mr. Baker's "I promise" still rings in my ears.

1961, May 24. Twenty-seven Freedom Riders are arrested as they leave the bus in Jackson Mississippi. In the seven months campaign, over 400 Freedom Riders are arrested. Many are sent to Mississippi's notorious Parchman State Prison where they endure difficult conditions intended to break their spirit.

Chapter 15

Ostracized

Kids at school know I'm pregnant. Principal Baker said so. A few days after he tells me the news, the halls are full of stares, giggles and whispers. Walking by, I know what they are about."She's pregnant you know. She's going to have a baby." Soon, the whispers turn mean. I don't have to guess about that either. After all, I'm not the first pregnant, unwed, fifteen year old girl at school. I have heard the nastiness before, even took part in it a little. Now, when I pass a group of students, including some I thought were friends, it's about me.

"Here comes the slut. Been screwin' around. Now she's having some guy's baby."

"Who's going to marry that bad ass girl?"

"Got a little bastard inside."

"What do you expect from a State kid?"

"Yeah, right. Who's your daddy, bitch?"

"She's a whore for sure."

"Who'd want to see that scarred up black bitch naked?"

"Yeah, let alone fuck her."

"Must have to do it in the dark."

"Heard she goes down for anyone. Doesn't matter what color."

"We'll know when the bastard comes out."

"Yeah, unless it's albino. You know, a combo kid."

And on, and on, and on.

During the last weeks of the school year, the walls of the girls' bathrooms get plastered with 'Bernie screws everybody,' 'Bernie's easy;' 'Bernie does Oxford;' 'State girls suck the big one,' and more. At night, Mr. Wilkin, the school janitor, scrubs the walls and toilet stalls clean. By the end of the next school day they're covered again with more profanity about me. Mr. Wilkin keeps scouring, but he can't keep up with the 'good girl' nastiness. I try not to think about what's on the boys' bathroom walls.

I refuse to show those mean kids how much pain I'm in; how much they are hurting me. I simply refuse! I walk the school halls with my head up high and my mouth shut. I do my sobbing in Mama Charles' arms.

Some adults are just as nasty, but they are clever about it. I know because, though Mama and Daddy Charles try to keep me from it, I overhear their friends' 'polite concern.'

"Oh, I haven't seen Bernie lately. Is she okay?"

"What's going to become of that one?"

"Is she still living with you?"

"You've tried so hard. But, some things, well you know—."

"You must be so disappointed."

By the end of the school year, things are worse. Parents and kids, who have been friendly, if not my friends, start to ignore me. When I say hello to them on the street, they walk right past as though I'm invisible. Some even cross the street when they see me coming. It really hurts when that happens. It is so different, so strange. In Oxford, I am very popular and have lots of friends. People know me for my athletic ability, my happy go lucky style, my curiosity about everything, and everybody. Sure, most folks know I am a State kid. But I live with Mr. and Mrs. Charles, so I must be okay.

But now, nobody phones or invites me anywhere. I spend the summer alone with my thoughts and my books. My changing body, my strange moods, and wanting to eat weird food really get to me. Thank God I have the Charles, and some family. Mama often comes to see me. Belinda tries to be supportive, but she isn't around the house much. She's off chasing her own dreams. When she is home, she seems more cranky than usual. Having a pregnant sister is, well I know my shame is hers too. She never says so, but being a State kid, I'm sure she gets nastiness too. Mama Charles is worried about both of us. She says our blood pressure readings have gone up. I've been to Dr. Reichart twice about it.

My worst summer since coming to Oxford finally ends. When school starts, I am there. I've got a little bump, so I let my blouse hang outside my skirt. Most people know why, so I'm not fooling anybody. Still, there's a new freshman class, so—.

Two weeks later it all ends. I'm called to the principal's office. Standing behind his desk, Mr. Baker says, "Time to go, Bernice."

"Okay," I whisper, fighting to be brave. Still, tears start streaming down my hot cheeks. Peering at him through wet, terrified eyes, I say, "I'll be back. You promised."

Principal Baker nods, but says nothing.

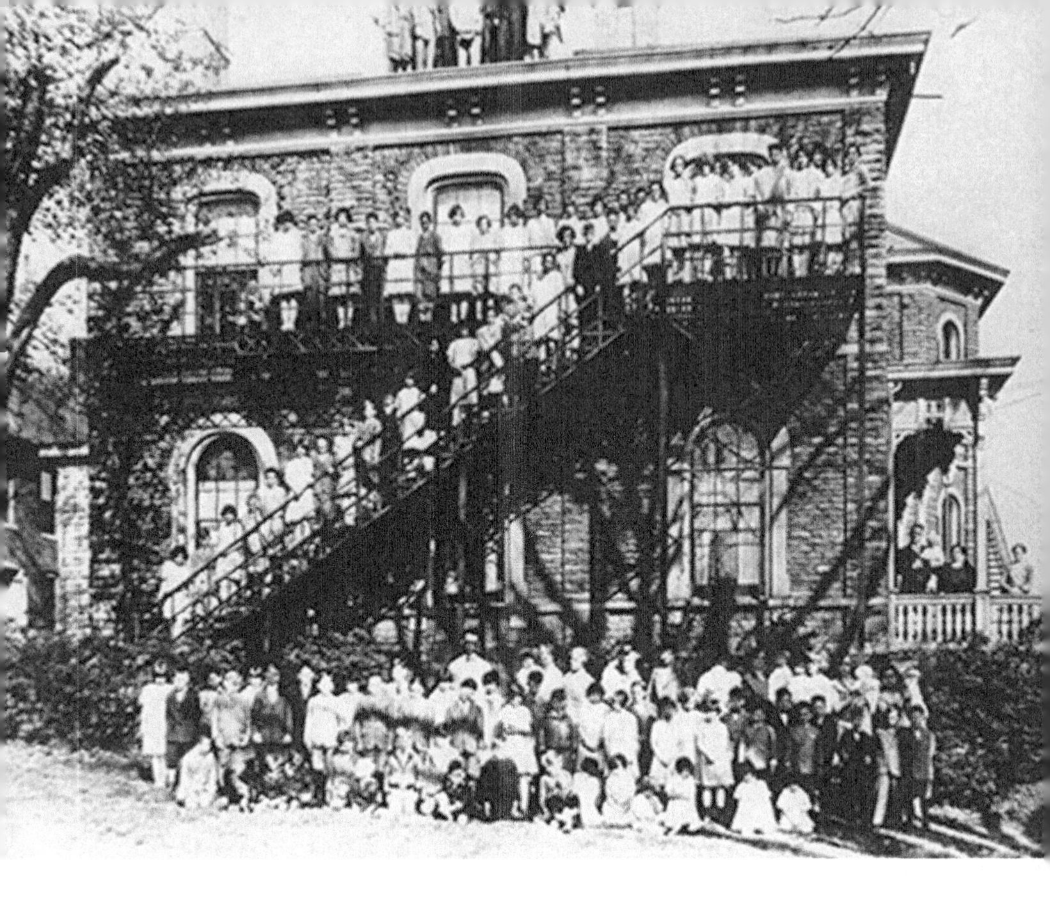

1962, September. A pregnant teen, Laverne McDay is forced to drop out of Talawanda High School. A Ward of the State, she is taken from Oxford Ohio to the Butler County Children's Home in Hamilton Ohio.

1961, May 24. Ohioans David Fankhouser and Dave Myers at Central State College in Wilberforce Ohio, and Francis L. Wilson of Cincinnati answer Diane Nash's call for volunteers to replace the original Freedom Riders who were injured in the bus firebombing in Anniston Alabama. Wilson, a student at Tennessee State University, is one of fourteen students expelled from the university for their Freedom Ride participation.

Chapter 16

State Kid–Again

It finally happens. The dreaded social worker picks me up and drives me from Oxford to a part of Hamilton that I have never been in or don't remember. After all, I was really young when I was taken from my mama and sent to Oxford. Now, I am back in Hamilton, back because I'm pregnant. I guess somebody told the State. This morning, Mama Charles did her best to explain. Wiping a tear, she said, "Miss B, no matter what Daddy Charles and I do or say, until you are eighteen you are a ward of the State. Because you are pregnant, they won't let us keep you no matter what."

Now I'm sitting at a large table in the crowded and noisy cafeteria of a dark old house full of mostly white kids. The room smells like, I don't know; fear I guess, just like Johnny's Devil House. It's been a long time, but I haven't forgotten. I look around and see that I am one of the older kids. If there's trouble, I probably can handle myself okay. Still, this place gives me the creeps.

Across the table is a small scrawny white boy. I guess he's about seven years old. He just sits there, staring at me with dark, sad eyes, one that's swollen. An older white boy sets a bowl full of something in front of me. The little kid's eyes go back and forth between the bowl and me. I guess he wants me to either move on the food myself or give it to him. Finally, pointing to the bowl with his dirty forefinger, he blurts out, "You want that lady?" I look at the bowl. I can't tell what it is, some kind of soup, maybe. For sure, it isn't anything Mama Charles would make. Nervous and not feeling well, I can't eat anything, whatever it is. I reply, "No, I—" Before I can offer it to him, he reaches across the table, snatches the bowl and jams it to his gap-toothed mouth. He gulps down whatever it is. His dirty fingers ring the bowl, finishing it off. It's as though he hasn't eaten for a while. My mind flashes back to a little girl with a swollen belly. The thought of starving or eating bad food again scares me to death. I think, girl, you need to get the hell out of here fast!

I move away from the table and go looking for the room I passed on the way in that has shelves with a few books on them. I'm hoping it's their library. Wandering down a dark hallway, I find it. Eyeing a big soft tattered chair in the corner, I plop down, sink deep into it, and close my eyes. Thoughts of Oxford, the Charles, some kids at school, and Walter race through my mind. My head starts to hurt almost as much as my empty swollen stomach.

*

A voice wakes me up. "Bernice, your sister Claudia is here to get you." I open my eyes and look around the lamp lit room. I must have fallen asleep for several hours. Two women are standing at the door.

"Who?" I ask.

"Me," a tall pretty brown woman says, coming towards me. "I'm your sister, Claudia. You don't remember me. I haven't seen you since you were a little girl. Mama sent me to take you to Aunt Mona."

For sure, I don't remember her. And I don't know any Aunt Mona either. But I don't care. I just want out of this awful place with all its lost and scary kids. "Okay," I say, jumping up. "Lets get the heck out of here."

On the car ride, Claudia says our mama paid Aunt Mona, who is 'family,' to take me in. I only have one question for her.

"Does Mr. McVay know where I am?" Claudia frowns and says, "Aunt Mona has nothing to do with that Johnny McVay."

*

I stay with Aunt Mona for several weeks. She last saw me when I was born, so she doesn't know much about me, or my life in Oxford. Still, she thinks I'm smart and tells me so. Maybe it's because I'm always asking her for books to read. I like being around her and her husband Raymond, especially since there's always stuff going on at their house. Aunt Mona, who is a huge, sassy, woman, is what folks call a 'hustler.' She comes up with lots of ideas about how to make a dollar. Right now, she runs a 'social club' in her basement, a card and drinking room for the neighborhood. I'm not supposed to know about it, but when 'Miss Curiosity' asked Uncle Raymond about all the people coming and going, he winked and told me.

For weeks, Aunt Mona never says a word about me being pregnant. I'm sure she knows. I catch her watching me, checking my body out and making sure I get plenty to eat. That's good 'cause next to Mama Charles, she's the best cook I know.

Then one day, we are upstairs in the bedroom folding clean towels. Suddenly, Aunt Mona stops folding and sits down on the bed. She looks at me in a way that says, 'I have something to say and you best listen.' She takes my hands in hers. Peering over her reading glasses, she looks me straight in the eye and starts in. "You know Bernie, everybody makes mistakes. And it's all right to make mistakes once in a while. But when you make mistakes over and over again, they turn into habits."

"Yes Ma'am," I reply. "But I—"

"Shush now and listen," she interrupts. The fat on her upper arms jiggles as she drops my hands and stares hard at me.

"Yes Ma'am," I whisper. She begins again.

"My girl, just because you got pregnant, yes I know you are pregnant, and you are going to have the baby. But you don't need to keep having babies, babies and more babies. You can go on with your life. You don't have to stop because you have a baby. You made a mistake, one mistake, a mistake."

I look down at the floor. As usual, talking about my pregnancy embarrasses me, makes me feel foolish. In fact I hate that word pregnant, it makes me want to spit up!

Aunt Mona reaches over and with her big meaty hand, gently lifts my chin.

"A mistake, you hear me?" she says softly but firmly.

"Yes Ma'am."

"Do you hear me," she asks again, even more forcefully.

"Yes Ma'am, I do."

And that's it. Aunt Mona grabs my hands and squeezes my fingers together. With a loud grunt, she stands and heads downstairs. Left alone, I start to panic, thinking about my pregnancy and future. Oh God, everybody's talking about this baby inside of me. Which by the way, I want out of me. But, I don't know how—how do you get a baby out of you? I don't really know how it got there in the first place. But, I do know I want it out right here and now. How can I do what Aunt Mona just said to do? After the baby comes out, how do I go on with my life? What kind of life will it be? It's all so confusing.

*

Weeks pass. My body begins to change a lot. I really notice it when I lie on my stomach. I feel a little ball. The older women, including Mama Charles, who come by to see me, start asking, "B honey, do you feel anything moving down there?" When I say, "No, nothing," they frown, pat me on the cheek, then go out into the hallway and whisper, "Seems like that baby is just growing to her."

I don't know what that means. Nobody talks about pregnancy much. It's all so hush-hush. I don't even know what to ask! I do know that when most teenagers are pregnant, the girl goes somewhere either for an abortion or to have her baby and then give it up. Either way she comes back with no baby. Not me. I'm having a baby and keeping it. As I said, Mama Charles and Mama gave me no choice about that.

The longer time goes on with nothing moving inside my belly, the more the women watching me seem to worry. I start to wish I'd been born on a farm. I could see how animals get pregnant and have babies. Maybe then I could figure out what's going on inside, or not going on.

Then it happens. Something in my belly moves. It almost feels like I'm digesting food. Aunt Mona is in the room. I tell her I feel something move in my stomach. Out she goes to tell two other aunts, who are visiting, and sister Claudia. From my bedroom, I hear the words 'quickening' and 'tightening' among the whispers. I don't know what those words mean. Heck, it's folks talking about me again, like I don't exist. I might be just a kid, but I have a right to know! Jumping up, I stomp out to the hall and yell, "Hey, what's going on? What does 'tightening' mean? What's 'quickening?' I hear you talking about me. Is the baby ready to come out?" Surprised by my yelling, Aunt Mona spins around to greet me. The other women duck behind her big body. "No Bernie," Aunt Mona replies in her straightforward way. "The baby is not ready to come out." She pauses, takes a deep breath and goes on. "Bernie, we—all of us—are worried you can't have this baby."

Shocked, I blurt out, "What? I can't have this baby? Why not?"

Sighing heavily, Aunt Mona pauses. Frowning at me, she explains, "Because of your burn scars. We are worried that you can't deliver the baby because it will stretch the stomach scars too much. Quickening does that."

Listening to her, I suddenly remember that 'can't' word. It's what the hospital doctors told me. They didn't think I could get pregnant, run fast or do anything physical. But I can do anything, especially run. And now I'm pregnant. So far they are wrong about everything. But this is something new.

"What are we going to do then?" I quietly ask. They all stare at the floor, saying nothing. Their silence confuses me even more. I turn, go back to my room and lie down on the bed. Then it hits me. I shiver as I realize what they don't want—can't tell me. If they can't get the baby out, then I—I could die! Oh God, I—this little baby inside me won't live. We're not going to live. I'll never see anybody again. I haven't even started my life yet! Now I'm going to—.

Frozen to my bed, I stare at the ceiling, thinking about what Aunt Mona said. I'm scared, angry too. How do those women know everything? They're not doctors, why should I listen to them? I mean, they're family but—. Why are they scaring me?

Questions I should have asked before pop into my head. I need answers, especially from those know it all women who say I'm in trouble. I bounce up and march to the hallway. The women see me and stop talking. I spit my biggest question at them.

"Hey, where is the baby going to come out?"

"Down there," sister Claudia says quickly, pointing to my crotch. "Out of the vagina. It's going to come out of the vagina. It's going to stretch—"

"Oh, heck," I cut in, "Babies are big. That's a tiny—you're saying the baby is going to come out down there?"

They all nod yes. I can't believe it. I don't know what the heck I've been thinking all this time. I mean—I know they come out somewhere. But really, I thought it was like 'open sesame—herrrre's your baby.' No sweat. But now Claudia says they come out down, you know, down there! That scares me even more. I don't really know much about things coming out down there other than pee. And once a month or so, there's blood. Not since I got pregnant though. And then there's my scarred up belly right above. That's what everybody's worried about, why I may not make it. "Well," I mutter, "Somehow, I'll just have to prove them wrong again!"

*

A week later, Mama Charles clears up another thing I've sort of been wondering about. Sitting in Aunt Mona's kitchen, we're holding hands, talking about how things are, how I'm feeling. Suddenly, she lets go of my hand. Putting on her serious face she begins.

"Bernie, some things need to be understood and decided."

"Yes, Mama Charles," I say excitedly. "I've been thinking—"

She puts her finger to my lips to hush me and starts in again. "Child, getting pregnant means; well, we know abortion is against the law. Still if one wants—. But abortion, say you don't have the money or you don't want one, is out. So then, you can have your baby but don't keep it. You give it to someone else to bring up so you can go finish your education or whatever."

"Yes?"

"Well, if none of that happens and you keep the baby, which you are, you get married—which you are."

1961. The United States Civil Rights Commission declares that Cleveland Ohio has a long history of police brutality. The Commission recommends 'professionalizing' the Cleveland police force and making local government liable for police conduct. Cleveland authorities ignore the recommendation.

1962, April 1. Civil Rights groups unite to launch a voter registration drive throughout the Deep South.

Chapter 17

Taking Charge

Okay, Sammy and I are going to get married. It's all being arranged. But until then, I am still under the court's control. That means 'the State,' whoever that is, still owns me. Being pregnant, they order me to have a physical checkup with their doctors at Ft. Hamilton hospital.

There are two doctors and of course they are white men. I don't know their names, but that's okay, since they don't seem to care who I am either. At least, they never say my name. In fact, they barely talk to me. Once again, it's as if I am not here. But I have lots of questions for them. When I ask, all they say is, "You're here to be examined, not ask questions."

After the examination, they tell me to wait out in the hall. Standing close to the door, I can hear them talking. One of them says, "We might do an abortion. But, she's a smart little cookie. She could cause us trouble at some later time."

It's the first time I hear the word abortion—a-bor-tion, related to me. I really don't like that word. It feels like someone is punching me right where my baby is.

"Abortion," I whisper. "Why an abor—"

Then it hits me again. It's true what the women at Aunt Mona's and the Mercy Hospital doctors say. They think I can't have my baby and survive. It's not about having an abortion to get rid of the baby. It's about saving my life! Shaken, I keep listening. The one with the deep voice says, "Okay, but if we don't abort, how are we going to deal with it? With those deep scars, I don't know about a C-section."

"Better than the alternative," the other says. "We should talk to her. I'll get her."

I scramble away from the door and sit down just as he appears. He motions for me to come in. "You are going to have your baby," the short one says. Then he hesitates, looks down at me and goes on, "Unless you want an abortion. We think it might be best if—"

"No," I cut in. "I don't want an abortion. I want to keep my baby. I—I WILL have my baby." Surprised, both doctors glare at me. I can tell they aren't used to anyone rejecting their advice, especially some State kid.

"How will you take care of this baby? You're just a kid yourself," the taller doctor asks. "It's going to be very difficult for you—"

"I WILL do it," I interrupt again. "If I have to scrub floors or whatever—I will take care of him. I WILL!" For some reason, I always refer to my baby as him. It just seems that I have a boy inside of me.

"Okay," he growls, turning his back on me. "It's your baby, your life."

The short doctor scowls at me and turns away too.

Leaving their office, I think, those State doctors, they don't get to decide what's going to happen to me. I do! No abortion for this smart cookie. I want that baby. No doubt it's going to be risky, dangerous even. Everyone says so, but so far they have all been wrong about me.

*

Two weeks later, Sammy and I get married. A terrified little kid, dressed in a green pinstriped suit with a pink flower in the lapel getting married to another scared kid in a suit and tie in front of some family. There are no friends. Mama arranges the ceremony at the Bethel AME Church in Hamilton. She's there, along with Mama Charles and Sammy's mother and father. That's all I remember about my wedding day. Not much, I know. Just going through the motions. Just glancing at Sammy when the time comes and quickly saying, "I do."

Afterwards, I think, hey, one good thing. I no longer belong to the State. Getting married ends all that. Nobody can taunt me about being a 'State kid' anymore. I mean they can, but it isn't true. Better believe I will tell them too.

After our wedding, Sammy and I move in with his grandma Heddy on the north side of Oxford. Except for his mom, who lives in Hamilton now, the rest of Sammy's family, including his father, live close by, down off Sycamore Street. They are all very supportive; wanting to help us 'babies' raise a baby when he comes.

I can tell right away, it isn't going to work. I am different, not just from Sammy, but all of them. Maybe it's because I got to live with Mama and Daddy Charles. They're different from these folks. Not better, just different, the economic thing. Or maybe it's just me.

Besides getting ready to have the baby, a lot of what I think about is my education, about going back to school. The thought of THAT education eats away at me. Something else is driving me crazy too. My bubba Walter, where is he?

1962, March 20. In an effort to politically compromise Reverend Martin Luther King Jr. and the Civil Rights Movement, the FBI wiretaps the NAACP office of Stanley Levinson, a white civil rights activist with alleged communist sympathies. In November, Attorney General Robert Kennedy authorizes the FBI to wiretap Levinson's home telephone.

1967. In Cincinnati Ohio, the New Orphan Asylum for Colored Children closes. Opened in 1895, the asylum's mission was to care for orphans as well as children whose parents were unable to care for them economically or physically.

Chapter 18

Finding Walter

For years I kept asking Mama about Walter, but she wouldn't say, afraid of what I would do, I guess, how it would affect me. But after my wedding, she finally breaks down and tells me what happened with Johnny and where Walter is now.

When Walter went back to that Devil House, at six years old, he was the oldest kid, so he got Johnny's worst. That little kid took it best he could, until at eleven years old my Bubba tried to burn that house down. I know exactly why he did that. In his mind that house was where all the bad things happened. If he could burn that hell house down, then they could move someplace else and everything would be good or at least better. But Walter couldn't burn that house down by himself. He tried, but got caught before the fire spread very far. After that he started getting into trouble in the streets, stealing stuff, fighting and of course drinking. The police always brought him back to Johnny and Mama. That's what they do; bring kids back to their 'respectable' parents. Walter caught even more hell from Mr. McVay, the respectable church deacon.

The older Walter got, the wilder he got. Bigger and stronger, he started standing up to Johnny. Thinking it best for her family, Mama gave Walter back to the State. They put him in the Longview Orphans Asylum in Cincinnati. He was thirteen years old.

After Mama tells me what happened, I start to visit Walter as much as I can. We have long talks about what happened to him and to us. Often he breaks down crying, "I should have stayed Bernie. I should have stayed with you. I thought—thought it would be better. I was just a little boy. I didn't know. Guess I hoped Mama would—could change things."

It breaks my heart, especially since now he is alone in this jail like place, waiting for someone to want him. So far nobody does, either because he has a 'bad boy' reputation or because nobody in the family can afford moneywise to take him in. I don't really know. For some reason Walter is a taboo subject in our family. Of course each time I leave him, I want to bring him with me. But being a teenager, I'm not allowed to rescue him from Longview, no matter how much I want to.

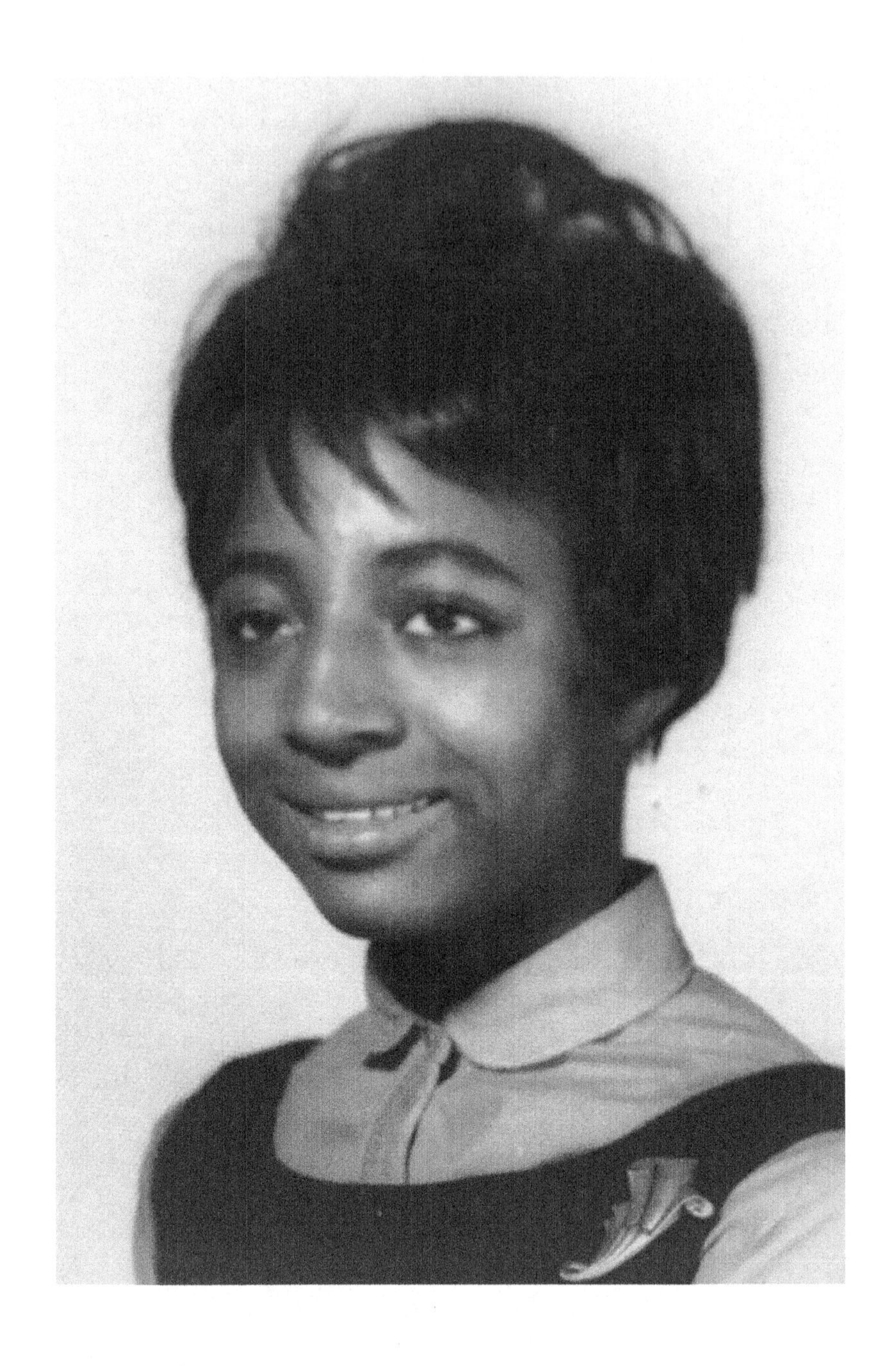

1962, October 24. Laverne (Bernie) Warren gives birth to Bryan Lamonte Warren.

Chapter 19

Baby Byran

Even though those State doctors checked me out, no one can believe I am carrying a baby because my stomach is pretty flat. The older ladies keep saying that my baby is growing into me, whatever that means, and it's scaring me. Being a teenager, high school drop out, married to a young man just a couple of years older than me, and living with his paternal grandmother, I can't really enjoy all the little niceties of having a child. Still, as the birth time gets closer, Sammy's family helps care for both of us. His grandmother Heddy Brock calls me Sunshine and watches me like a hawk to make sure I don't harm the baby or myself. Apparently, a miscarriage is a real possibility. Miss Brock's sister Lori is a nurse, and she also checks on me.

*

It's late October, about two months after seeing the State doctors. I'm at home resting and trying not to think about the C-section I am scheduled for at Fort Hamilton hospital next week. I know what that means now, makes me really nervous. But the doctors, including Dr. Reichart, say it is the safest way for my baby to come out and even with my belly burn scars, best for me too.

I get up and go to the toilet. As I bear down, I feel a sharp pain 'down there,' like my menstrual cramps. "Aaaaggg," I scream as another wave of pain hits.

"Grandma, the baby is moving way to much! Aaaagggg, what's going on?"

Grandma Brock rushes into the bathroom. Her big eyes are wide open—scared looking. She puts her hand on my belly and says, "Your stomach feels like contractions. I think you better get to the sofa. That baby may be coming. I'll call Lori. We might have to deliver this baby. Michael!"

Michael, who is Sammy's cousin and a high school student, is at home. Hearing his name, he rushes to the bathroom door. "Get Bernie to the sofa and cover her up," Grandma says. "I've got to get on the phone!"

With me screaming even louder, Michael helps me off the toilet and carries me to the living room sofa. By now my belly scars are hurting almost as much as my inner 'down there' parts. Grandma comes in and says, "I'm boiling water. Lori says we are going to have to deliver the baby."

Hearing my screams, three college students passing by the house rush in to see what's going on. Michael shouts, "She's having a baby, go get blankets off the beds—back there." They head for the room where Michael is pointing and quickly come back with bedding. Michael covers me up. I'm screeching even louder, trying to scream the pain away. Next thing I know Oxford police officer Jones is here saying the Life Squad is on the way. My screams have turned into moans so I hear Grandma tell Jones that Dr. Reichart is coming. Then, pulling the blanket to my neck, she whispers, "Take your breaths girl, and hold on tight." She starts counting.

The Life Squad arrives and takes over. With one big push, my baby shoots out and into the hands of a Life Squad man. I lift my head and peek between my legs. I scream, "Oh no, he's—" I stop myself from blurting out what I see; that I've given birth to a monster! The baby's hair is so long and dark that it covers his face and shoulders. The umbilical cord is dark green, and the baby is covered with some cottage cheese looking stuff. He lets out his first ear splitting scream. "Wwwwaeeeeeeee!"

Dr. Reichart arrives. Winking at me, he immediately examines the baby. Cringing, I close my eyes as he snips and clamps the cord, then orders him wrapped in blankets. He quickly checks me 'down there.' Finished, he smiles and says, "Bernie, you did well. He's a beautiful boy. We'll see you at the hospital." Taking the baby in his arms, he rushes out of the door.

The Life Squad cleans me up and takes me to the hospital. After being stitched up 'down there,' I am put in an isolation room. I'm really tired—still scared too. I'm wondering, where is my baby, why can't I see him? I haven't even held him yet. Is he all right? Am I okay? I don't understand any of this. Why isn't he with his mother, and me with my baby? It's very confusing. I never thought it would be like this. Why is it this way? I'm so frustrated, exhausted. I close my eyes and sleep for hours.

When I wake, I am still alone. Groggy, I wait for someone to check on me, tell me what's going on. Finally, a smiling Dr. Reichart comes in. I bombard him with my questions. He sits quietly, waiting for me to finish. When I ask, "When can I see him?" he explains, "We need to keep the baby and you apart because your home wasn't a sterile environment, so you and the baby could be what is called 'germy." I nod. Then Dr. Reichart says the best thing, "Your little boy is okay, just premature, so his body weight is low. We need to keep a close watch on him for a while. He is in an incubator in the nursery just down the hall." Since I'm germy, I can't leave the room to see my baby. The nurses tell me everyone at the hospital wants to see what they call 'the little Collins baby,' especially since he is the first baby delivered by the new Oxford Life Squad. Of course Mama, the Charles, and Sammy's family do too. Even Bobo's mother, who volunteers at the hospital, comes to see him. But no one is allowed near him except the nurses. When they stop by to check on me, I ask, "How is he doing? What does he look like?" All they do is look at me and say, "You have a beautiful boy." Then they go about their business. I don't get that. I think, hey, is that all you have to say—to tell me—his mother? That's it? How about telling me something I don't know. But they won't.

*

For three days I lie in my room, a little scared and wondering if something is weird about my baby. Finally, on my fourth day in the hospital, a nurse brings my baby to me and places him in my arms. He is wrapped in a blue and white blanket and has a small blue scull cap on. His hair is dark brown and about three or four inches long. He has bright green eyes—and white skin! Shocked, I glare at the nurse and stammer, "I—I—t—think you brought me the wrong baby. This is somebody else's baby." Frowning, she says, "I'm so sorry. Let me check." She takes the baby from my arms and leaves. Minutes pass. She returns and carefully hands me the same white toned baby. She smiles and says, "I checked Bernie. This beautiful little boy is yours."

My heart leaps. Now I know what the nurses wouldn't say. They know I'm married to Sammy, but from the baby's color, they thought the father was white. They—they thought I—no wonder they had nothing to say to me. What they didn't know, and I forgot, is that when I was born, I was a pink tone color. And that's really what he is, only lighter. That's probably because Sammy is lighter than me.

I look at him and he looks up at me. He cries a little. I laugh and kiss him, hug him, put him to my bosoms. With tears running down my cheeks, I whisper, "I will never let anyone take you from me again. I will keep you safe. Thank you God for bringing me something to call my own." I hold him up to my face. He looks into my eyes, into my soul, it seems. The light pink color is so beautiful, but like his mama's, I'm sure it will turn brown. I check his hands and feet, counting his fingers and toes. He has ten each.

I'm still recovering 'down there' and my belly scars are sore, so I tire easily. I give my baby back to the nurse until later in the day. I can't wait to hold him again. I lie in bed thinking, knowing that at fifteen, my life has changed. As I told those State doctors,

I will do everything I can to be a good mother for my sweet baby boy. No matter what happens between Sammy and me, I will never regret having him or anything about him. I am glad God picked me to be his mama. He is my blessing from day one until forever.

Sammy comes to the hospital to see us together for the first time. We talk about a name. Sammy doesn't seem to care much, so I name him Byran. I read it means 'strong.'

Two really nice things happen when we get out of the hospital. Byran is the first baby delivered by the Oxford Life Squad. So, Officer Jones and Mr. Phillip, who heads the Life Squad Department, get to appear on the popular Ruth Lyon and Bob Braun show in Cincinnati and tell the audience about my baby boy. Also, several Oxford stores give us baby gifts. That's pretty cool. And for our young family, it helps a lot!

1964, June. Volunteers from the Mississippi Summer Project meet in Oxford Ohio for training in nonviolent discipline before heading into the Deep South to register Negro voters, set up community centers and teach in freedom schools. Three volunteers, James Chaney, Andrew Goodman and Michael Schwerner go missing on the first day of the Freedom Summer in Neshoba County Mississippi.
1965, September. Teenagers Victoria Nash and Pamela Walden enter the eighth grade at McGuffey Junior High School, Oxford, Ohio. The school was legally de-segregated in 1951, but Miami University officials employed 'administrative policies' to discourage Negro students from attending.

Chapter 20

Life With Sammy

Probably the kindest thing I can say about Sammy is he never says he isn't my baby's father. He really can't because he knows I was a true virgin. That's something I can love about somebody. But with Sammy that's it. As far as life with Sammy, well right off it's pure hell. I wish I didn't have to say that, but it's true. I want it to be different so bad but—.

After Byran is born, we move to Indianapolis, Indiana where Sammy's mother, Ruby and stepfather Maurice live. We have no money so we move in with them. Maurice says he can get Sammy a good job. The trouble is, Sammy's mother spoiled him rotten so he doesn't know how to do much. That upsets her, so she and Sammy argue a lot. I just go about my business with the baby, trying to stay out of it. Finally, Maurice comes through with a job for Sammy.

It's obvious I'm not what Sammy's mother planned for her son, her baby boy. It's the 'State kid' thing for sure. Too bad for her, I have Byran. She tells me she wants custody of him, says Sammy and I would be better off. Okay, maybe so, but no way I'm giving my baby up to anyone.

After a few months, Sammy, the baby and I move to our own apartment in an old German neighborhood that is changing from white to mixed race. Sammy isn't around much. After work he heads for the streets. It's like the streets call his name, making sure he doesn't grow up, which he isn't. I have parent responsibilities, so I have to grow up fast. Sammy doesn't help with Byran or with anything really. I wish he did, but he won't. He loves sports, so he is always off playing some kind of game, baseball mainly. I like sports too, so I don't mind really. But Sammy never invites Byran and me to his games. From the beginning of our marriage it's like Sammy has his life and I am just the maid with a baby.

Ignoring us is not the biggest problem. I wish it was. The bad boy Sammy I was warned about is here. At home, he's always mad at something or somebody, usually me. When he drinks, which he does a lot, he yells, cusses me out, and calls me names. Most often it's motherfucker or bitch. He really likes to call me Miadiddy. That means somebody who is trying to get up on someone, be high class, put their ass on your shoulder. He does that just because I still want to get my education and better myself. You'd think he'd be proud of his wife doing that, but he isn't. Bad boy Sammy hates that and I'm paying for it big time.

Now that we are away from his mother's house, Sammy's getting physical with me. Most often it happens at night when, after putting baby boy down, I go to sleep. Sammy comes home drunk, wanting to fight. Cussing and screaming, he shakes me awake, grabs my hair and tries to tear it out of my head. He tries to pin me against the walls, the floor, anywhere. But I fight back! I'm pretty strong, so I do okay fighting him. I punch and kick, trying to get him in the crotch where it hurts the most; get him to bend over and stop. Fighting back makes me feel better than just taking it—not good, but better. It's not what I want to do. Of course, I'm getting the worst of it. Soon my body is covered with bruises, cuts and scratches. I have a chipped tooth and I'm sure my nose is broken. But I keep on fighting best I can. Lots of times we go toe to toe, punching, grabbing, throwing things, and even biting. I'm doing everything I know to get him to stop. Sometimes I can. Trouble is that's when he goes to get his shotgun, cocks it and puts it right up my nose! Hell, I don't move. With my baby boy right here in the house, there's nothing I can do. I'm scared if Sammy gets crazy enough, he'll shoot both of us. Hard as it is, it's better to surrender.

I tell myself I haven't done anything to deserve Sammy's throwing things and slamming me around. Still, I find myself wondering; am I'm doing stuff that makes him mad? Does he want me to stand up to him, even fight him so he can excuse what he is doing to me, to us? Maybe that's why Mama was so weak around Johnny. She didn't want to give him any more excuses for what he was doing to us kids. Whatever, seems I'm in the same place Mama was.

Of course, I'm supposed to be quiet about what they call 'bedroom stuff,' but I'm not. I call the police. Yes I do! On the phone, I scream at the police for help. Sometimes they come, but often they don't. When they do come, they don't do anything. They just say, "We don't get involved in domestic disputes." Going to the police station doesn't help either. They just say, "There's nothing we can do," and send me back home. I've had blood running down my face, gashes on my head and all they say is, "We don't get involved in domestic disputes." That's when I scream, "If you do nothing, you are involved!" I don't think they know what I mean, because they look at me like I'm the crazy one.

Even when the police do something, it's worthless. Several times the officers have come to the house, see me all beat up, and tell Sammy, "Mr. Collins, don't do that again." Other times they ask him to leave the house for a while to 'cool down.' They never tell him he can't come back. Of course, he returns madder than hell. I lock the door, but he gets in and starts up on me again. It's like the police will just let your husband beat you up—kill you even!

Well, that's not going to happen to me! Yes, I'm married to Sammy, but I've got to get away from him, the police, this whole mess. Problem is, there's no place for beat up wives to go. At sixteen years old, I've got no job or money, so running away is out. And run where? My closest girl friends are going through the same thing. My sisters and brothers can't afford two more mouths to feed. Plus, who's going to believe me anyway? I'm his damn wife! So I'm stuck. All I can do right now is try to protect Byran and myself best I can. I start keeping out of Sammy's way and doing little things to please him, like putting food out, and tiptoeing around. I never ask Sammy where he's going or been, no questions that might upset him. That means I never know where he is or when he'll come home drunk and start in on me. Of course, my big concern is Byran. I'm doing everything I can to keep him out of Sammy's way. Yes, I'm 'Bernie the Warrior' again. I hate it!

Then one day I find a letter Sammy wrote to a woman named 'J'. I read it. It's actually a lovely letter. It's the first time I knew Sammy could write. Even before we moved to Indianapolis, I suspected Sammy was seeing other women. Now I know for sure. The next day, sitting together in his new 1957 Chevy Bel Air, I show him the letter. All he says is, "I knew your damn nose would get you in real trouble one day. Now you're in it." Scared, I quickly scoot out of the car. Screeching his tires, he drives off. I think, wow, now that he knows I know about his women, it's only going to get worse. I need to take care of my baby all by myself. The question is how?

*

I was right. Since the love letter, Sammy is crazier than ever; so wild that the neighborhood people can't help but notice. Of course, they won't interfere. But several women and men tell me to take my baby and get away from him, say I'm smart and can do okay by myself. Some older folks even tell me, "You don't need that crazy nigger. He's no good for you." I sure know that now. The problem is, being on my own takes money. Sammy is working, but no money ever comes my way. Of course I can't go to his mother. Like Sammy, she is always out on the streets. Anyway, she'll only say, "I told you to give that baby to me."

Living with Mama and Daddy Charles, I learned to do lots of things. But I'm still too young to work. Then, thanks to some nice people telling lies about this underage kid, I get a job at the

American Linen Supply Company. My job is emptying the sheets and uniforms from the big carts. It's not hard work except that I'm so short I often fall into the cart when I try to reach stuff on the bottom. Everybody thinks it's funny. After two weeks of falling in the cart, my boss gives me a stool to stand on.

I work during the day, so I decide to go to night school at Arsenal Technical High School, a very famous school, to get my high school degree. Going at night will help me avoid Sammy too. But it also means riding the city bus thirty-two blocks out and back, and getting home really late. Thank goodness, Byran's grandfather Maurice and others look after my son, including Sammy's younger brother Danny, who is just out of prison. He loves Byran and does more for him and me than Sammy does. Still, on the nights when I am at school, I'm not always sure how Byran is going to do. It's too much for me. Hard as it is, I give up on school for now. Tell myself—I'll be back!

*

Sammy wants to go back to Oxford. So after two years in Indianapolis, we head back to Ohio. Sammy's mother moves too, but to Hamilton. Unfortunately, until we can get an apartment in Oxford we have to live with her again. She still wants Byran for herself and uses my dream of an education to talk me into giving him up. She says, "Bernie, let me have the baby. Then you can go to school or work. You'll be much better off without having to take care of him." I don't like hearing that stuff. I need to get away from her and her son. Thank goodness, Sammy's grandmother and Dad find a little house to rent on Oxford's north side. It's close to them and some friends who don't like what's going on with Sammy. So, one morning I decide to go for it. Making sure his mother and Maurice are in the house, I tell Sammy, "I'm leaving—taking Byran and moving to Oxford." Laughing, Sammy says, "Damn bitch! You think I care? Go, I'm staying in Hamilton."

Wow, I think, didn't expect that, but okay. Before Sammy can change his mind, Byran and I leave for Oxford's north side and move into a little house on Homestead Avenue. I'm hoping that living twenty miles apart and Sammy busy running Hamilton's streets with his buddies and women, he will leave us alone.

*

It's not working! We're still married so Sammy shows up at our house anytime he wants, mostly in the middle of the night. He busted out a window I can't afford to fix, so he can get in. Doesn't make sense to fix it anyway. Byran and I share the bedroom, so I try to at least keep Sammy out of there. If I can't, he goes after me right in front of Byran, smothering me with bed pillows or beating on me. Sometimes I wake up and can keep Sammy out of the bedroom. We usually go at it in the kitchen. His favorite thing now is to hit me over the head and back with the heavy dish rack. I've got the scars to prove it. Lots of times, he grabs my neck and chokes me. I think he has injured my voice box; my voice sounds scratchier and deeper than ever. When Sammy's stumbling drunk, I can fight him off. Trouble is, when he's losing, he gets really crazy and starts looking for the butcher knives, swearing he's going to cut me up. So far he hasn't found where I hid them, but—.

I can't do this! Desperate, even hysterical, at times I could kill that man. Really, me, little good girl Bernie wanting to kill somebody, take Sammy out, make the world a better place. Thank goodness, a voice inside me keeps me sane, warning, "Don't do it baby, he's not worth it. Kill Sammy, you'll end up in jail for sure and Byran left all alone. Then what?"

So yes, I'm trying hard to drop that murder idea, hoping Sammy will stop; just go away. But he keeps coming around; screaming, cussing, hitting, kicking, whatever. Each time we go at it, I'm back to wanting him dead!

I can't keep doing this, fighting him off, going back and forth about doing something terrible and stupid. Got to do something else before it's too late, but what?

*

It's morning. I wake up and realize I hadn't been dreaming. Sammy broke in last night, crazy drunk as usual. He snuck into the bedroom and woke me out of a deep sleep, tried to smother me again. I managed to escape and make it to the kitchen. It took an hour of screaming, begging, shoving, but I got him to go to his dad's. Thank goodness Byran was at his great-grandmother Nina's house, so he didn't have to see us fighting again; his dad drunk, mean, crazy, his mama cursing, crying, hitting, kicking—at her wits' end.

I head to the kitchen. It's a total mess. I sit down at the table to cry my eyes out before I clean up. But I'm too upset, too mad to cry. I'm thinking those awful thoughts again, knowing I won't hold out much longer and wondering: how in the hell did I get here? Memories flood my brain when, out of nowhere, I remember a promise made long ago. I think; is it my way out? To survive, save Byran, myself? Fighting back a flood of tears and fears, I blurt out, "Girl you have to! It's back to Talawanda or—"

1967, June 12. Protesting police brutality and poor living conditions in the black community of Avondale, Ohio (Cincinnati) crowds fill the streets and firebomb businesses. The Ohio National Guard is brought in to stop the violence.

1968, January 1. Carl Burton Stokes takes office as Mayor of Cleveland Ohio. Mr. Stokes becomes the first Black mayor of a major US city.

Chapter 21

A Promise Kept

Byran is almost four years old when I call Principal Baker and tell him I want to come back to finish high school. Since it has been a few years and one baby later, I remind him he promised I could return anytime the high school doors were open.

"After all this time and— Are you sure?" he asks. "Nobody expected you to—"

"I'm very sure," I interrupt. My stomach is jumping all over.

*

The day I decide to enroll I am sooo scared. I mean, why wouldn't I be? The last time I was in high school I wasn't treated very well. Who knows what's in store for me now?

I ask my ride to drop me a block from the school. I say good-by and walk towards Chestnut Street. I turn a corner and suddenly there it is—Talawanda High School. The buildings look the same. It's what's inside them that I wonder, am nervous about. I hesitate, take in a big gulp of air and start walking down the sidewalk to the main building. I stop in front of the big double doors. As usual, my nervous belly makes the scars tingle. I reach out and grab the door handle. I panic. Suddenly it feels like an electric shock zapping my hand. I let go of the door handle and spin around. Eyes watering up, I hurry back to the street corner. I stop, turn around and stare down at that school. Several seconds pass before I wipe my tears away and mutter, "Okay, let's try this again."

I walk back and forth seven times. Yes, I am counting! I want so badly to go through those doors, but each time I can't. Finally, heading down the sidewalk one more time, I say, "This is ridiculous. Just do it girl." Nervous but determined, I approach the doors, grab the handle and with all my might, pull hard. The door swings open and almost hits me in the face. Off balance, I fall in. Yes, that's how I go back into my old high school—falling through the front door! Picking myself up, it feels like a thousand pound weight has been lifted off my shoulders. As I brush myself off, a woman comes down the stairs to greet me. She's smiling. Apparently all this time, the office staff was watching from their window, waiting for me to get up the nerve to enter the building.

I am sooo happy. It isn't starting school that's tough. It's just going through those big doors. When I left Talawanda, I had gone out the same doors, crying my heart out and feeling a whole bunch of things, especially that my life was ending and I didn't know what was going to happen to me. Being pregnant, I was leaving in disgrace. A lot of people inside were thinking, well there goes the State kid. We should have expected this to happen, blah, blah, blah.

Now that I'm back through those double doors, all the bad memories don't matter. I'm so excited. It is where I want—need to be! I look down the main hall. The kids are coming out of class. I see my friend Ronnie Tucker and yell out, "Hey Ronnie. It's me." As the boy walks closer, I see he isn't Ronnie. I guess my mind wants so badly to be where I can see my friends again, to be comfortable, in that 'other' moment, as I call it. Okay, I get it. It's the same place, but different time and different people, including me. Still, I don't care how or if I'm going to fit in. I don't have any choice. I've got to get out of the trouble I'm in. And yes, I've got to finish what I started.

I go into the office to enroll. A woman staffer asks me lots of questions, what have I been doing, where have I been, things about my life in general. I tell her some things, but not all of it. I tell her I want to finish as quickly as possible. She sets my schedule to do my junior and senior years at the same time. Of course, it's up to me to do it. Whew.

It isn't until I actually start taking classes and all, that I can see high school is going to be very different this time. I am the oldest student in the school, married and have a child. For some reason, the kids seem to like me, even adore me. Not everybody, but the juniors and seniors for sure. I'm sure the freshmen and sophomores don't know what to think. Having lived life a little, they probably assume I know everything. I have to be careful what I say to them. They are so naive. I don't want anyone to think I am here to spoil their innocence. You know, the old lady with the baby, telling 'secrets' kind of thing. Thank goodness, Mr. Baker and his staff can see that I am going to be a good girl, not mess with the younger kids. They trust them to be around me, to actually 'love on me.' And they do. Of course, plenty of the kids are curious about my time out of school. I don't tell them much, especially what's going on with Sammy, who still comes around being his nasty self. Mostly they wonder how I go to school and still take care of Byran. Sometimes I bring him to school. The teachers and kids just adore my 'little man.'

Still, there isn't anyone for me to really just 'hang' with. In that way school the second time around is a little lonely. But, as the weeks fly by and I get past being nervous, I start having a good experience. The taunts I got when I was pregnant aren't there this time. And I'm working hard, crazy in fact. I don't run track or anything like that. I just study. Everyone, the faculty and staff, and most students seem to want me to make it. In fact some of the guys; both Colored and white, write me little love letters or whisper in my ear wishing me well. Some folks might think they are trying to get in my panties, you know the slut thing again. I don't take it like that. I just think they are honest. And if they aren't, well getting into this girl's panties is not going to happen anyway. Not this time.

What is really great is that my teachers, some who hadn't bothered with this Colored girl before, now treat me like a real student. Beginning my second and senior semester, they call me in to talk about college. I can't say they are doing the same for the other Colored kids, but as for me, I am the center of their attention. Mrs. Drassy says it's because I am the first dropout with a child to come back to finish high school. When I get the English Award and the Artist Award, the counselors are all very excited. They know I can't go to college without financial help. Thank goodness, because of my good grades, I get a scholarship to Miami University and other financial aid. My biggest prize is to be one of six recipients of Miami's first-ever Martin Luther King Jr. Scholarship.

Things are going so well, I can't believe it. So far Sammy isn't messing with us. People say he's in Hamilton doing 'his thing.' Great! But if he does try his nasty stuff again, I've got an escape plan. Hopefully, it will work 'cause I've had it.

*

Of course Sammy eventually finds out I'm back in high school. I sure didn't tell him, but Oxford is a small town. He can't stand it. He starts showing up at Talawanda, peeking in windows, trying to embarrass me. After school, he hangs with the young girls, dating some of them even though we are still married. I guess he thinks I care. I don't. Why the school staff lets him on school grounds, I just don't get. Maybe he sneaks on. He was always good at sneaking away from school. Now it's the opposite. Anyway, all I know to do is hold my head up high and try to protect my baby and myself from all his stuff. I can't, I mean, I won't let him screw this up.

*

One morning, I wake up with the word 'divorce' buzzing in my brain. I don't know how it got there. It's like some Holy Spirit woke me up and said, "Get a divorce." I don't know anything about how to do that. But I know Mrs. Stratten, my librarian friend does. I go to the library, tell her that I am thinking about a divorce but don't know how. "Are you sure Bernie," she says. I nod at her. She smiles back. We don't say anything, but I know she knows why. She goes to her desk and writes something. She comes back and with a smile hands me a note and her car keys. "It's in Hamilton," she says. "You start with a lawyer."

I'm not real clear about what a divorce will mean, if anything, so I take my time driving to Hamilton. On the way, I think hard about my situation, again realizing I really have only one choice: get Sammy out of my life if I can. If divorce will help with that, I'm going for it. By the time I reach Hamilton and find the Rencher Building I'm more determined than ever to go through with it. My plan is to tell the lawyer what I want, no hesitation, and see how it goes. Entering the building I find the directory. For some reason the name Norman Grevey jumps out at me. "Okay, let's try him," I mutter. I go to Grevey's office, meet him, and after a brief discussion about my 'situation,' he asks me, "Divorce, are you sure it's what you want?" With no hesitation I reply, "I'm sure—very sure."

"Yes, you do seem very sure," he says. That's it. Mr. Grevey agrees to start my divorce. My plan worked. I'm on my way.

Driving home isn't so easy. Thinking about what should have been with Sammy and our little family, my hopes and dreams, makes me very sad. Twice, tears blur my sight so much I have to pull off the road. The second time I begin to have doubts about a divorce, wondering if a piece of paper will make any difference to Sammy or anybody. "Doesn't matter," I blurt out, starting up the car. "Little man and I need to move on: best get rid of the Devil's urge to do his dad in."

*

Graduation day is finally here. This day is very, very important for everybody, not just me. I am the first one in my family to graduate from high school. Everybody else had to quit school to work in the fields of the Deep South or Ohio factories.

I hear Sammy told everybody, "No way I'm going to that Miadiddy's damn graduation." That's fine with me. Mama and Daddy Charles are here, as elegant and proud as ever. Mama, who finally escaped from Johnny's abuse, comes with them, as beautiful as ever. Lots of siblings from Hamilton and Cincinnati also come. They take turns fussing over little Byran. Best of all, Walter is here! A few months ago, he walked out of Longview Orphanage Asylum and back to me. Now, at eighteen, he is a grown man, physically strong and amazingly mature. If he's bitter, he doesn't show it, even though he was abandoned for five years. How he overcame that and Johnny's messing, I don't know. He just did. Yes, he did! And he's so proud of me. "Love you Bernie," he whispers, giving me a big hug. "Love you more Bubba," I reply, wiping a tear away with the sleeve of my graduation gown.

I've never been to a graduation ceremony before so I just do what we rehearsed. When it's time to hand out the diplomas. I wait nervously for my name to be called. Finally I hear "Mrs. Bernice Collins." As I cross the stage to receive my diploma, my family and friends start clapping. I hear Walter's wolf whistle. Of course my nervous belly is doing its usual tingling and twitching all over the place. This time I don't care; my scars are doing their thing underneath my graduation gown. A man I don't know gives me my diploma, smiles and shakes my hand. Walking away, I see Principal Baker smiling at me from his place on the stage. He steps out, grabs my hand, gives me a wink, and whispers, "Congratulations Kitten." I want to hug him, squeeze him to death, but I know I shouldn't. Choking up, I nod and walk off the stage to my chair. Sitting down, I remember to move my tassel to the other side of my cap, a sign I am a graduate. I think, yes world, I am a graduate. Finally, hard work, my curiosity, and yes being darn stubborn—telling them what I want, paid off for me, and for Byran too. High school is only our first step. Next up is Miami University. I'm so excited! And scared too, about college for sure, but more about that damn Sammy.

1968, April 8. Riots erupt in Avondale Ohio at the end of a service celebrating the life of Martin Luther King Jr. who was assassinated on April 4, 1968. The riots begin in response to gunshots and rumors of a white police officer killing a Black woman, and are sparked by pent up anger in the Black community over the slow progress in civil rights. Twenty-four hours later a curfew and the arrival of the Ohio National Guard end the rioting.

1968, September. The Office of Minority Affairs (OMA) is established at Miami University. The purpose of the OMA is to support minority-sponsored activities and help overcome the traditionally conservative white-oriented campus culture. Eighty-nine Black students enroll for Miami's Fall semester.

Chapter 22

I'm Black and I'm Proud

I'm twenty-two, almost twenty-three when I enter Miami University as a freshman in January 1969. Last year was full of tragedy. In April and June, Dr. Martin Luther King Jr. and Senator Robert Kennedy were assassinated just weeks apart. The Vietnam War is killing more and more people on all sides. Anti-war protests are spreading across the country and onto just about every college campus, including Miami. Still, it's an exciting time for many people, especially us young Negros, I mean Blacks. The new Black Power movement says 'Negro' and 'Colored' are whitey's names for us; say it's about racial oppression. So, I—we are Blacks now. It's okay with me.

I am so excited to be in college! Who could imagine it, a little State kid going to a big university or any college? Of course I'm very nervous. I'm one of the first recipients of Miami University's Dr. Martin Luther King Jr. scholarship. That absolutely shocks many people in Oxford, especially my own 'community' of Black leaders. In my last days of high school they took one last shot at me. One of their social clubs has a little $100 scholarship that is supposed to go to the minority kid with the best grades. That was me. But they refused to give me the award. They wouldn't say why of course, but everybody knew. I have that baby. Plus all the other things they hold against me: my blackness, a State kid, and the 'bad girl' thing. Mama Charles belongs to that darn social club. When they refuse to give me the award, she walks out—won't go back either. Mama Charles doesn't mess around. She's from south side Chicago and won't put up with that blackness prejudice stuff, especially when it hurts her 'kids.'

Anyway, I get the King Jr. award. That's what really matters to me. I mean: it's about Martin Luther King Jr.! So the pressure is on. I feel like all of Oxford's eyes are on me. I just know they're wondering; will the State kid make it? Does she deserve our support? Or is she just some uppity black single mother trying to do the impossible? And of course there's always the 'anymore bastard kids' coming along?'

On campus, I start to meet other students, mostly Blacks, but a few whites, from other places. Many of them, like Larry Clark and Paul Payne, who are leaders in the Black Student Association, are from big cities like Cincinnati and Cleveland. Some are from the East Coast, mainly New York City. I meet some international students too. They and the big city students are so sophisticated. They have a different take on things, such as the idea of freedom, the right to be who you can be and so forth. It's what Mr. Jacks has been talking to us kids about, especially finding our identity. It fits my personality, so I quickly grab on to much of what they are saying.

It's a fun time, being with new people, talking to fellow students and studying with them. But it's hard too. I have a jam-packed life for sure. Like regular students, I'm going to school fulltime. But when I leave campus I go into the world of being a single mom to my precious Byran. He needs me around and I crave his constant love. We also need to pay bills, so I get a part-time job at the local hospital. I'm so lucky to get that job! I get to know a lot of new people, medical professionals mostly. Many of them support what I am trying to do. They even collect a little money for us when we are in real need. I'm keeping a record so I can pay them back when I can. The person I really admire is Mr.

Tom Kane, the hospital director. When I start the job, my shift begins at four o'clock in the afternoon. But because I ride my bike from campus after class, I am always a little late. One day Mr. Kane is at the door, tapping his foot and scowling at me. In his stern voice he says, "Mrs. Collins, what am I to do with you? You are always late to work."

"I'm sorry, Mr. Kane, I ride as fast as I can, but—"

"No excuses," he cuts in. "If you don't get to work on time—well, I don't know."

"I'm sorry," I say, rushing past him and into work. I am sure I will be fired if I am late again.

The next day, I peddle as fast as I can from campus, but I'm still five minutes late. Mr. Kane is waiting at the door with a piece of paper. I jump off my bike, park it and go to get fired. Sure enough, Mr. Kane hands me the paper. Trembling, I stare at it. It's my new schedule, and it says I now start fifteen minutes later. Mr. Kane smiles at me and disappears into the hospital. After that, he is on my side even after I pull a lever that floods the surgery room, leaking water to the floors below. The repairs cost thousands of dollars. Turns out, it isn't my fault. Someone had failed to turn a key or something. Mr. Kane starts calling me 'Miss Disaster.' Thank goodness, he's kidding.

The doctors, especially Dr. Samuels, and the nurses, are very helpful too. They let me use the hospital medical library to study for my health science courses. They even put up with all my medical questions. If I have to study for an exam, some of the nurses will cover my floor duties for me. Hey, I'm just a nurse's aide. They don't have to do that. Of course, they just love Byran, the kid some of them met in his first hours of life.

*

To me, campus life is exciting but weird. Miami University is a very white and conservative campus. It's where the all-white fraternities of the 'Greek System' started. The 'Greeks' still pretty much run campus political and social life. Due to the racist stuff, Blacks are excluded. Of course, we are 'free' to have our own Greek clubs. Miami also has a famous sports history, especially its football program. Black athletes are recruited to run fast, shoot baskets and score touchdowns. Otherwise, there are few non-athlete Blacks on campus. As I start my freshman year, I read that sixty-seven of Miami's ten thousand students are Black.

Besides being a non-athlete, my situation is very different from other Black students. Being a 'townie' from the 'hick' town of Oxford, there's no way I can be as 'hip' or 'cool' as the big city 'sisters and brothers.' Plus I am the only single mom. Nobody else has worry knots twisting their stomachs up over their baby boy, or rides a bike around campus with a kid on the handlebars. None of them have to ask their professor's permission to bring their kid to class and hope he sits quietly, or figure out what to do when a professor says I can't bring him. That happens a lot.

The 'bad' girl rumors follow me to Miami. Many 'sisters' don't like me at first. Of course, the 'brothers' are way too friendly, 'popping up' wherever I am, looking to get 'close' to 'Miss Ice.' It's what they call me. I'm not stupid. I know what those silly boys are hoping for.

Soon folks get to know me and what I'm about. I make some good friends. They adore my 'little man' Byran. Much of our social life is sitting at a table way back in corner of 'The Res,' the student center cafeteria. It's the 'Black' place on campus. We talk, laugh and play cards. Whites also go to The Res, sit at their own tables, doing the same things. It isn't 'forced' segregation, like the swimming pool or movie theaters I knew growing up. It's the old 'understanding' that people sit with their own kind. Except now with the Black Power movement on campus, it's Blacks who want segregated spaces. So far I don't hear any white people complaining, probably because Oxford is full of 'white spaces' at the uptown bars and restaurants. Most Blacks who drink alcohol do it at our north side house parties.

The idea of Black Power is new to me. I mean, I've always been proud of my race, but now we talk about it. For the most part I get along with whites, so sometimes I get caught in the middle.

Since high school, I've become close friends with Bobo Grosscup, I mean Beau. Ha! I'm now Black, he's Beau. On one of his trips home from graduate school, I take him to a north side house party. He's the only white person there. No matter what I say, it's clear he isn't welcome, so we leave.

Since there are only a few Blacks at Miami, I'm not sure what to do or say, if anything. I mean, I don't mind going out on a limb like I did with Beau, but—. Then I discover some things about my, that is our, unique place at Miami University that help me decide what to do.

*

One morning, I slump down at our Res table before a full day of classes. I'm really tired from working till midnight at the hospital. Plus, I woke Byran up to say goodnight, I mean hello. I don't see enough of him.

"Wow, I'm beat," I say to the four sisters sitting at the table. "I'm thinking I should cut my morning class once in a while and sleep in. It's in a big auditorium, so nobody will notice I'm not there." The sisters stare at me in amazement. Then Shawna asks, "Girl, how many students are in that classroom?"

"It's a big lecture hall," I reply. "About 300, I guess."

"How many of us are there?" Frieda, another 'sister' demands. I'm confused.

"Us?" I say.

"Blacks," Frieda sneers. Suddenly I get it. My mind races around the classroom. I see only my black self. "Just me," I reply.

The whole group cracks up. "There's your answer," Shawna snickers. "Girl, you stick out like nobody's business, especially as dark as you are. Every time you miss class, they know."

"That's right," another sister chuckles. "They already know who you are, where you came from, maybe even your name—" Shawna cuts in, "Yeah, those white professors may not know anyone else in that big class, but they sure know about you, Bernie. They know about all of us. I mean, of course they don't 'know' us, but they sure do see us."

I'm stunned. I know on campus we are a minority, but I never thought about how that affected whitey's world. Of course they know who we are. It's like we are black islands in a white ocean. Physically, I—we really stick out. Of course my professors 'see' me.

I had forgotten, but the same was true in high school. Blacks were a definite minority, so of course whitey 'saw' us. That's why we had to act in that 'acceptable' way, always on guard. After I got kicked out of high school, I lost track of the 'race thing.' I had lots of other things to worry about, like staying alive. When I was allowed back in Talawanda the push for Black awareness was new. There still weren't any Black teachers or any books or classes about Black life or history at Talawanda. Yeah, we learned about President Lincoln freeing the slaves; how he freed us. That's it. I guess we didn't do anything, just sat around waiting for whitey to get it together. I know from my books it's not true. Anyway, I was just glad to be in high school trying to graduate.

I guess I just thought things would be different at the university. I mean, it is 'the university.' But here we are again. I see no Black professors. The Black graduate students are a few African guys who pay big bucks to get in and a few sports graduate assistants. There are no Black studies courses. There is nothing here about me, about us, to see or hear about or to study. Education is about whites and what they did or do, so Blacks are still invisible. But in the great white ocean, like my Miami classrooms, on the street or grocery store, even at the hospital, I am always seen. We are visible and invisible at the same time.

"Well, that's disgusting," I mutter. I get up to go to class. Since I am the only Black on the roll sheet, I have to go. Walking there, I am so disappointed, feeling stupid. Well, I'm not stupid, but why did it take the 'sisters' to point this out to me? And now that I know, now that my eyes are opening, what should I—what can I do?

During class, I squirm in my seat. For the first time I am really uncomfortable being there. I need help. It's been awhile, but after class, I go to the one person in Oxford I know I can count on for that.

1969, December 3. The FBI, assisted by a 14-member Special Prosecutions unit, assassinate Black Panther leader Fred Hampton with two shots to the head while he slept next to his pregnant fiancée. Hampton is set to merge the Black Panther Party with the Blackstone Rangers, a community-service oriented south-side Chicago gang, which would double the membership of the national Black Panther Party. Documents connect J. Edgar Hoover and other top FBI officials to the raid and cover-up.

1969. Miami University creates the Office of Black Student Affairs. The program is intended for the educational, social and professional development of Miami's Black students.

Chapter 23

Franklin Jacks University

When I stomp into his office, Mr. Franklin Jacks is sitting in his big chair, pipe in hand. He rises and after a hello and quick hug, I get right to it.

"You know what? There's nobody at Miami for us. There are no Black professors, no courses about us—nothing. Everybody's white. Everything is white!"

Mr. Jacks frowns, looks towards the ceiling and then turns away. His back to me, the only sound is the tap, tap of his finger pushing tobacco into his pipe. Then he lights it up. Waiting, I think, great, he's thinking hard, coming up with one of those nuggets of wisdom I count on from him.

Blowing smoke into the air, Mr. Jacks turns back to me and quietly asks, "What are you going to do about it?"

I'm caught off guard. Hey, I think, don't be throwing stuff on me. That's not the way it works. I'm here for you to tell me what to do. Frustrated, I send some 'attitude' back at him. "Me? What do you mean me? Me—I'm just me. I'm a kid—a girl. What the—me?"

For a few seconds, Mr. Jacks stares at me, calmly puffing on his pipe. Then he asks again, but more firmly this time. "What are you going do to about it? You know about it. It's not new to you. We know that. So what are you going to do about it?"

Now I'm really confused, and getting uptight. Hot sweat rolls down my cheeks. I raise my voice. "Mr. Jacks. Why do you keep asking me what I'm going to do? I came here for—"

"You know about it," he interrupts. "Do you like knowing about it? Do you like the feeling of it? You know about it now. So what will you do?"

I can't stand this. I try to stare him down. He stares back, waiting. Damn, I think, he's throwing that question at me again and again. The one I have no answer for!

Frustrated, it takes a few seconds for me to remember who's doing this to me and why. Franklin Jacks bombards you with questions. He doesn't just give answers. He doesn't tell you, "Go burn the mother down!" He does say that at times, but we all know he doesn't mean it like that. He means burn your mind up. Get to work doing something about it. Don't burn the buildings down. Burn the bad things out of them. Put back something better.

Saying stuff like this has made Franklin Jacks the most controversial person in old-fashioned Oxford. He challenges people, especially us young Blacks, gets up in everybody's face and makes them think. As a Black man that is double trouble, especially now with the Black Power movement making noise, the Black Panthers, white hatred of 'uppity' Negros, and all that. But all Mr. Jacks wants is for Blacks to hold our heads up and do what we think is right. It's like the new James Brown rap, "Say it loud, I'm Black and I'm proud!" It's why Oxford's Negro leaders, the NAACP types, and whites say he's a troublemaker. Well, he is a troublemaker. But to me, if there were more people like Franklin Jacks, Oxford would be better off. Most places would be.

Breaking the silence, Mr. Jacks really goes after me. "So, you know about it. You like it? You comfortable with it?" Man, I don't like him doing this. I know he wants me to say something back at him, show him some attitude; that I care. I spit it out, "No, I don't like it!"

Raising his voice even higher, Mr. Jacks barks, "If you don't like it, do something about it!"

"Hey, how can I do anything about it? What do I kno—?"

"Think about it, young sister. If that situation makes you uncomfortable, then work on what you want. Why are you so bothered that you've never had a Black professor? Been going on a long time."

"I DON'T KNOW!" I shout.

"Come on now," Mr. Jacks says, a frown on his face. His tone is stern but less harsh. He pauses, putting a match to his pipe. I'm still upset, but as he starts to speak in his 'teaching voice,' I calm down and start to listen, taking his words in like a sponge.

"You know nothing ever got done by being timid. If you are afraid, it's not going to happen. You can be mad inside, let things lie there. Until you bring it out so somebody can hear what you're saying, you have nothing. You've got to reach down somewhere inside of you and pull it up. You say they don't want to hear? Make them hear. Get their attention. Then tell them, not what you think you want, but what you want. Don't go there until you know for sure what you want. Don't ever go—"

Changing into baby talk, Mr. Jacks says, "Oh, I think, ah, maybe I want Black studies. Can we, would it be okay with you if we hire a Black professor or maybe two?" Back to his adult voice, he says, "Always say what it is you want. Be strong and be clear." Speechless, I stare at him. His tone turns even softer but still firm.

"Bernie, don't come here not knowing what you want. If you know what you want, got some ideas, then great. I want to hear them. Otherwise, you are just wasting my time. Now don't be wasting my time young lady."

I'm back being really uncomfortable. Wasting his time? I'm wast—? I don't know what to say or do. I just know Mr. Jacks is pressing me like never before, saying things I never thought I'd hear from him, treating me like, well, like one of them!

Pulling on his pipe, Mr. Jacks looks at me and asks, "Tell me, why are you going to school? What do you want to be?"

"I'm going to get my education," I quickly reply. It's my stock answer.

"Oh really," he grunts. "What kind of education? What are you going do with it, once you get it? What are you going to do when you leave Mother Miami?"

Again, his questions come fast. I realize I have no answers for him. He knows it too. Smiling, he walks over and gives me a quick hug. "Just think about it young sister," he purrs. Our talk is over. As I turn to leave, he waves at me and continues puffing on his pipe.

*

Well, thanks to Mr. Franklin Jacks, I now know what the questions are that need answers. I also know I can't just sit on the sidelines while my, I mean, our 'seen-not seen' situation goes on. I join the Black Student Organization and begin protesting the lack of a Black presence on campus. We push hard for our cause, holding meetings, talking to and debating with Miami's sea of white students, faculty and administrators. We bring in Black activists from other campuses, like the poet Don Lee from Cornell University, to help. And of course we march and march, and march some more. We also take a stand against the Vietnam War. With white students, we organize a sit-in in Rowan Hall against the Reserve Officer Training Corps (ROTC) that turns really ugly with police dogs and arrests. Then, to show our power, we convince lots of folks to flush a toilet at the same time. The 'flush-in' completely drains the uptown water tower, causing pipes to break and buildings to flood. Nobody has any water including the fire department. Everybody in Oxford is upset, including my hospital friends. I tell them, "Hey, it wasn't me who turned on the showers and flushed all those darn toilets in the student dorms."

It's hard to be out there, going against everybody, especially when the university and police threaten us with arrest and suspension. I could also lose my scholarships. But, it has to be done. I admit, sometimes things get a little crazy. The flush-in was really stupid and most people know it. But lots of people blame us Blacks for it—and it wasn't even our idea. They say the flush-in, along with how we dress, our Afros, whatever, and the campus changes we are pushing for, only prove how 'militant' we are. Of course, in whitey's world that's not allowed. Also, talk about stupid. At one rally, with little Byran tugging at my skirt, I grab a poster without paying attention to what it says. That evening Mama calls, saying I was on Hamilton television carrying a 'Fuck Mother Miami' sign. I'm shocked, that isn't an answer I am going for. For sure that isn't what Mr. Franklin Jacks had in mind either. Thank God for him.

1972, November 7. Barbara Jordan and Andrew Young are the first Blacks elected from Southern states to the United States Congress since 1898.

1972. Wayne Embry, a Miami University basketball legend is named Vice-President and General Manager of the National Basketball Association's Milwaukee Bucks. He becomes the first Black person in the United States to run a major white-owned professional sports team.

Chapter 24

Sammy–Still

At Miami, I'm growing, learning, and doing all the things I ever dreamed of. But Sammy is still a big problem. Things are getting worse, in fact downright scary again. We are divorced, but that means nothing to him. He is always around the house, says he wants to "catch up with my damn kid." My first semester on campus, he makes it his business to find where my classes are so he can stand outside the windows and shout all his nasty stuff at me. Why university officials let him do that I don't know, but they do. Guess it's the old "we don't get involved."

One day I come home from school to find Byran dragging his leg around the kitchen. Sammy is there. He had agreed to stay with his son until I got home.

"What's wrong with Byran's leg?" I ask. Sammy gets up from the table and says, "Damned if I know," and stomps out of the house.

"Come here little man and let me see," I say to Byran. He drags his leg over. Lightly rubbing his foot, I ask, "Where does it hurt?" Byran opens his mouth but says nothing. "What's wrong with you?" I ask. He doesn't answer. Then I see something on his tongue.

"Baby, what's in your mouth?"

Byran spits whatever it is onto the floor. I pick it up. It looks like some kind of meat.

"Byran, what is this?" He still won't talk. "Okay, until you tell me what's going on, you stay in your room." Byran limps off to his bedroom.

An hour later Sammy comes back, high as usual and wanting dinner for babysitting. "Okay," I say, "but I need to know what's with Byran."

"I gave him some sausage for breakfast. Kid put the meat in his mouth but wouldn't swallow the damn thing; said it was too hot. Kid's as stubborn as his damn mama."

I let it go. After dinner, Sammy heads out for the streets. I get Byran, sit him down to eat and ask again what happened. My seven year old is ready to talk.

"Dad wanted me to swallow a hot sausage, but I was afraid it was going to burn my insides. He made me stand in one spot till you got home. It made my leg hurt really bad. He told me not to tell you."

Now I know why my baby's leg ached. Also why the inside of his mouth was white. Sammy has never laid a hand on his son, but if Byran starts acting out, especially not doing what his dad wants, there's no telling what will happen. I'm mad as hell and back to thinking those horrible thoughts. Standing at the kitchen sink, I lose it.

"I'm going to take a knife and kill that nigger—take him out tonight!"

Spinning around, I see my Byran staring at me with huge eyes. He is scared to death. "I didn't mean that, little man," I say quickly, trying to calm down. I grab him and press him close. "Mama didn't mean that baby. Everything is okay." But it isn't. I know that if I don't do something different, Sammy's going to kill me, or us. Last week he waved a shotgun in my face and snarled, "One of these days I'll walk past you and blow your brains out!"

*

A week later, things get really nasty two nights in a row. The first night, Byran is at his grandfather's. I'm alone in the kitchen studying for an exam. It's late but still really hot, so I'm naked. The back door slams and Sammy is suddenly in the kitchen. Crazy drunk, he starts in on me. "You fucking bitch! What the hell you doing sitting 'round reading for? Still think you're better than me? Shit, about time I make sure you're not." Looking around the room, he snarls, "Ain't no fucking people saving you this time bitch."

Something tells me to go, don't fight him this time. Before he can grab me, I jump up; tear through the house and out the front door. Naked, I sprint through the neighbors' yards to Sammy's dad's house where Byran is. I'm so dark nobody can see me. I don't care if they could.

I knock on Dad's door. He lets me in. Glancing at his nude daughter-in-law, he quickly locks the door. I run to the bathroom; grab a big towel and wrap it around my body. "What's going on?" Dad yells from the front hall. I go to tell him.

"Sammy's at the house. He's out of his mind. Says he's going to kill me." Dad grabs me in a hug and says, "Don't you go back there. Stay right here."

Someone is pounding on the door. Dad looks out. It's Sammy. Twisting the doorknob, he yells, "Let me in. I need to talk to that damn bitch."

"No," Dad says. "Get away from the door—best go home now."

Minutes pass. From the front room we can hear Sammy cussing and working the lock with some tool. Finally, he gets in. Dad meets him in the front hall. I'm standing in the living room scared but ready to help Dad. Sammy swings his leg up, trying to kick Dad in the crotch. Missing, he snarls, "Get your ass out the way you gray headed son of a bitch. I want my wife!" Sammy tries to push past, but Dad grabs his arms, spins him around and shoves Sammy outside. Slamming the door shut, he yells, "No more. Don't ever come back here!"

Heading upstairs to check on Byran, I think, that's it for Sammy and his dad. It's been a long time coming.

*

The next morning, I wake Byran and with Dad go back to our house. Sammy is gone. That same night Sammy tries again. This time Byran is asleep in the bedroom. I hear Sammy tapping on the living room window. I sneak into the bedroom and gently wake Byran. Quietly, he gets up and pulls on some pants. We are ready to get out fast. It's our new survival plan.

Sammy goes around to the front door. Instead of cussing me out, he says, "I know you're in there. Please let me in. I just drank a bottle of shoe polish. I need help."

I know it's a trick. I want to shout, "Good for you!" But Byran is shaking, so I need to hush. I pull him close and wait. Sammy starts banging on the front door, and yells, "Open this mother fucker or I'll break it down."

"Time to go," I whisper. Taking Byran's hand, we scoot out the back and run through the yard over to Mrs. Summer's house. We call her 'Mamasan' because she knows how to handle 'business.' Living next door, she knows what goes on; wanted us to have an escape plan. We're doing it.

We stop next to her garden and wait. A crashing sound tells me Sammy has broken the front door glass. Looking over, I see lights go on inside our house. I turn and run to a half open window over Mamasan's flowerbed. I whisper as loud as I can. "Mamasan—Mamasan, Sammy broke into the house. He's out of his mind."

Mrs. Summer looks down from the window. "Come around front," she says. We run to the front porch. The door opens and Mamasan and her man Dent meet us. He says, "I should go over there and bust that—" I cry out, "No Dent, don't do that." Just then, the big yard light comes on at my house. Dent says, "I'm calling the police."

Half an hour later, a police car pulls up in the driveway on the side of Mamasan's house. Watching my house closely, I see Sammy run out of the front door and disappear into the dark. The police go over, look around my yard, but don't find him. Knowing Sammy, he's probably up a tree or some fool thing like that.

The police come back to get me. Sammy's dad joins us. He saw the police pull up and knew it had to be about Sammy. We all go back to my house. There is blood all over the broken front door. It has to be Sammy's. Still, the police check Byran and me out for cuts. This time, because we ran, I have no new ones.

Over the next three days, nobody, including some of my family, can find Sammy. That's good because I know if brothers Bobby or Walter get to him, they'll snap his neck for sure. Finally, I do something I should have done before. I go to the police station and file assault charges against Sammy. It makes me feel a little better, but sad too. I have to do it.

*

A few days later I get a call from Sammy's mother Ruby. She knows what's been going on with Sammy and me, but always says, "Don't want to interfere; not my business." This time she knows it's serious. Over the phone she yells, "Drop the charges or I'll take Byran away from you. I know things about you. I know you're not a good mother."

I'm stunned; don't know what to say. I think, did she really say, "You're not a good mother?" She said that about me?

Now I'm mad—madder than I've been in a long time, ready to do her in too. I never thought she'd go after me, threatening to take my son, telling people I'm a bad mother. No way I am!

Standing there holding the phone, I realize what a fix I'm in. Ruby is desperate, wants to save her son, so she'll try anything. The problem for me is, I'm on scholarship. I can't afford any bad news floating around about me. Plus, they won't keep Sammy in jail very long. He will come jack me up, maybe Byran too. I have no choice. Seething, I spit into the phone, "Okay I will drop the charges—but you are not getting Byran. You will never get him."

*

Sammy gets out of jail mad as hell. He starts up again, but now it's all the time, so Byran is caught in it. After two weeks of drunken late night brawls, I finally get it. If the 'system' won't do anything about Sammy, I have to. I decide to take my, our life into my hands. First, I move out of the Homestead house into one Sammy doesn't know about. I hear he's trying to find us, so it's only a matter of time. Next, I swallow my pride and ask family and friends for help, for protection really. I don't want to, it's embarrassing, but I have to. Some folks start to come through, especially Terry, a Miami football player and new man in my life. Despite my busy life, we go out a few times. Twice, once at a north side party and then later at my new house, Sammy shows up drunk and screaming, "She's my damn wife, I get to talk to her." Both times, Terry scares the dickens out of him. I must confess I start to feel a little sorry for Sammy, the father of my child. But then I stop, just can't do it anymore.

At home things start getting better, but it's not over. On campus, Sammy still finds me and yells nasty things with people around. But off campus, I have Big Will, a neighbor who's a couple years younger than me. He has taken to being close by when I'm alone. I hear that Big Will, who wouldn't hurt a flea otherwise, told Sammy, "I will smack you upside your head if you don't leave her alone. All she's doing is going to school, so leave her alone." I can just see Big Will's green eyes flashing as he said that. When they flash, he's ready for whatever.

All of a sudden I have protectors. Terry, Big Will, even boys, now men, I knew growing up, help me. A few of them are always so drunk they can barely stand, but they can talk some 'bad shit,' as they say. Liquor courage, maybe. Most know Sammy, know they can whip him if they have to, know he's got a gun, too—.

The university finally gets some kind of restraining order against Sammy. I don't know what took them so long, but all my professors are on alert, and the university police are shadowing me, making sure I am safe. And, thanks to Terry, the Black football players are ready to 'clock' Sammy if they see him around campus. Bless them, but I hope that doesn't happen.

All of these people make me feel safer, but it's family that finally ends it. On Christmas Day, Sammy comes to the house.

Drunk and swearing, he throws all the presents out in the yard. I get ready to fight him. "Damn you," I shout. "Byran bought those—"

Byran interrupts and says, "It's okay Mama. I'll get you another present." He looks over at his dad, unafraid. Caught off guard, Sammy stares back in disbelief, then growls, "You a damn fool boy." Turning to me he mutters, "Next time I'll bring my damn shotgun." He throws one more gift into the yard and stumbles out to his car.

It's the last straw for my Walter. He comes up from Cincinnati and lets it be known he's looking for Sammy. Knowing Walter well, Sammy gets smart and moves to Detroit.

1972, January 25. Representative Shirley Chisholm announces her candidacy for President of the United States. A Democrat, Chisholm becomes the first woman and Black person to run for President as a candidate for one of the two major parties. Her campaign slogan is 'UNBOUGHT AND UNBOSSED.'

1972, June 23. President Richard M. Nixon signs Title IX into law, providing women equal opportunity as men to attend the school of their choice and develop the skills they want.

1973. The National Black Feminist Organization is founded to deal with the unique racial and gender problems of Black women.

Chapter 25

It's My Body!

In my second year at Miami University I decide to major in Health Education. I really like working at the hospital, but it's more than that. I also want to make a difference in peoples' health. I should be able to do that as a health educator.

Wow, talk about sticking out like a sore thumb. I'm the only Black person in the program, very visible here. As usual, I have my own way of thinking and doing, so it takes a while for people in the program to get me. But, that's been going on most of my life. As far as I know, I'm the only mom.

But there's also something I've never had to deal with before. I don't know how to describe it, except to say, "My professors love my body." Really! What I mean is, they are fascinated by how I am made up physically. In my physiology and kinesiology classes, or any class that has to do with the body, the instructors point at me and say, "Now take Bernie for instance—blah, blah, blah." When they do that, the other students, who are all white women, turn around and stare at me. It doesn't matter what muscles we are studying, they still stare me down. It embarrasses me. I silently beg, please don't do that.

They keep on doing it, so being quiet isn't working. I decide to take Mr. Jacks' advice and tell them what I want. Next time it happens I say, "Hey, I'm not special. I think everyone has the same muscles." But my instructors don't care. They keep telling me, "Bernie, no one here has your physique, your muscles, the way they are." I guess I'm supposed to be happy they think I'm special, but I'm not. In fact, I hate it!

My body really fascinates Miss Kile, a physiology instructor. She's very certain about how and why my muscles are different. One day in class, she says, "Now remember Bernie, under every curve lies a muscle. There are developed muscles and underdeveloped muscles. You have developed muscles."

I can't let that go by. I ask, "Miss Kile, what does that have to do with anything? Where are you trying to take this?" She doesn't like that for sure. She scowls at me and says, "You should be flattered."

Flattered? I don't think so. It's like I'm a specimen or statue they feel free to inspect all over whenever they want. It's like the African woman Saartjic Baartman I read about. White Europeans 'loved on' her body too, especially her big booty. Some animal trainer even put her in his 'freak show.' Well, I'm not a freak. Like me, I bet she wanted to scream, "Hey it's okay once in awhile to point at me and say, 'look at that physique.' But every day?"

It's not just in class either. Somehow word of my 'unique' body gets around. Maybe I'm getting paranoid, but it seems like people are staring at me all over campus and in town. When I pass the uptown stores people actually come out and gawk, even point at me. I don't know who told them about what's going on in my science classes. I've lived in Oxford a long time, so why all of a sudden am I so special? Why can't my professors accept that my muscles are from doing 'boy' things; climbing trees, riding bicycles and running around the Bluffs? I mean—I was a track star.

I start wearing ugly baggy clothes to hide whatever it is they find so amazing. It helps, but I still feel like I'm on display. People, I must say mostly whites, keep staring at me. It makes me think back to what I read about the slave markets. White owners put slaves on a pedestal and ordered them to "open up your mouth, turn around, flex your arms, let's see your legs," so they could figure out how much money they were worth. People in Oxford aren't looking at me for that reason, but—.

Still, there's no way I can stop people from staring if they want to. And since I usually dress nicely, going around in oversized clothes also draws attention. Some Black sisters even accuse me of going 'hippy.' They laugh at me and ask, "What's up with that girl?" I feel caught in the middle of two worlds again.

Finally, some political activist friends come to my rescue. Like being Black, they tell me to be proud of my body, to appreciate it. I decide they are right. I'm lucky. I've got muscles and curves in the right places, a high tight booty too. For sure I'm not going around saying, "Look at me." I just won't let those stares embarrass or scare me anymore.

So I stop hiding in big ugly clothes and start to be 'woman body' proud. I guess it's working because when the famous poet, photographer and Black activist Don Lee comes to the university to help the Black Student Association, he asks me to represent the image of a beautiful Black woman for his photographic exhibition. For hours I pose for him dressed in elegant outfits. I'm thrilled! Still, I wish my professors would stop using me to teach about the body's muscle structure, showing me off. But, being a student there's not much I can really do.

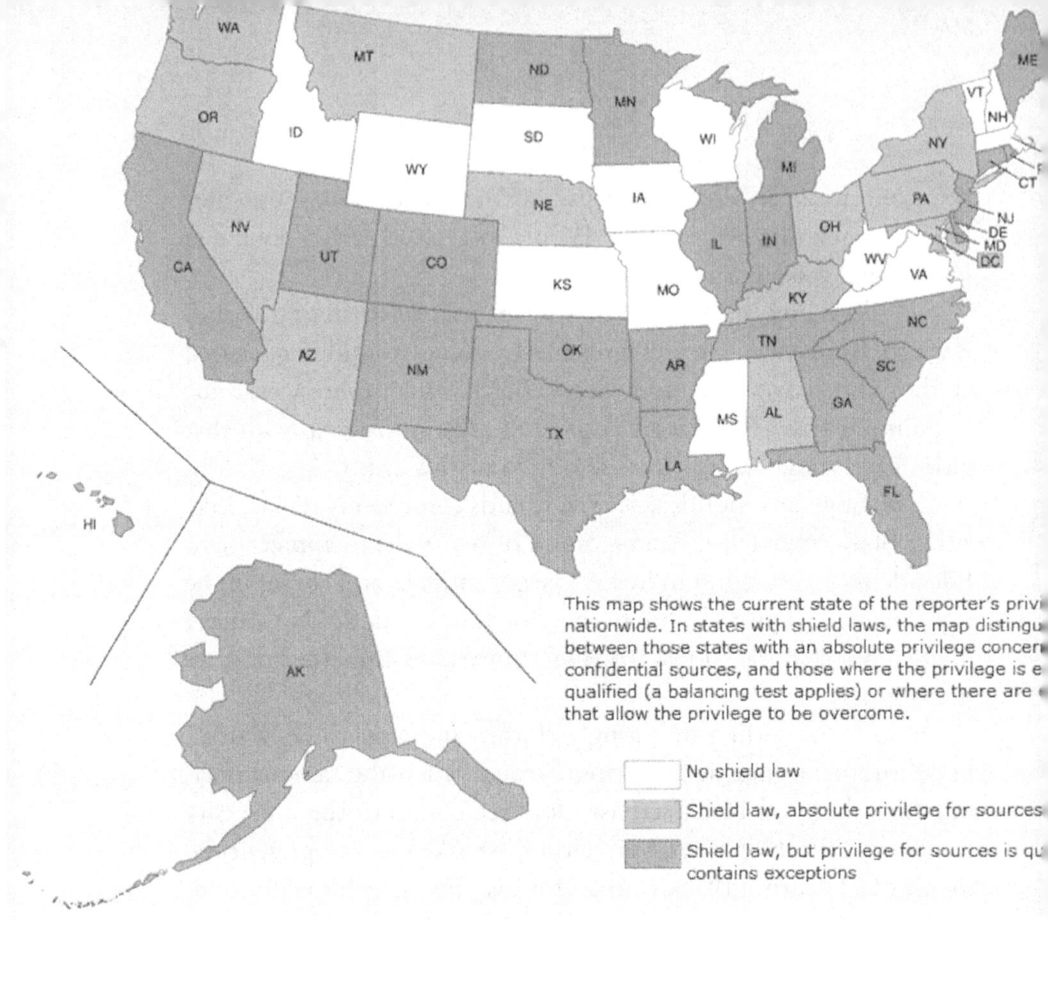

1970. Pushed by the Feminist Movement, State governments begin to consider Rape Shield Laws that limit the admissibility of a rape victim's sexual history at trial, thereby eliminating the bias against a rape survivor for being sexually active. Rape Shield Laws are intended to encourage rape victims to come forward knowing their sexual history will not be an issue at trial. Michigan passes the first Rape Shield Law in 1974. Ohio's Rape Shield Law is adopted in 1975.

Chapter 26

The Pillow Rapist

After my sophomore year, my brother Billy gives me a car, a used Buick. One night someone pushes the Buick out of my driveway and drives off. I don't know who stole it, but whoever did, they drove across two state lines to Tennessee and crashed into a deep ditch. Some Indianapolis friends go to Tennessee, pull it out, bring it to Indianapolis and fix it up. They tell me to come get it. Hooray!

I ride a bus to Indianapolis. From the bus station I take a taxi to my friend Susan's house where I'm staying. She has an upstairs apartment in an old house. The apartment has what is known as a Florida room, a large roomy space with big windows where everyone gathers. I really like that. Susan has four kids, two teen boys and two little girls, age four and three. I am to sleep in a bedroom with the girls. Since I am going to be there for only one night, they pull down the hide-a-bed for me.

Susan and I spend the evening in the Florida room, watching the little girls play, and laughing about our lives. Before we go to bed, I take two pain pills for my headache. They help me sleep really sound. That's probably why I don't hear the intruder.

Something wakes me from a deep sleep. Somebody is on top of me. A pillow is forced onto my face. I can't breathe. My mind goes to Sammy. I think, damn, how did—. I feel something sharp pricking my neck. A man's voice whispers, "No sounds—hear? I will kill you and the kids."

It's not Sammy. If it was, I would fight like hell. But now I just need to breathe. I force my head to the side so part of my mouth is free of the pillow. I work my eyeballs, trying to see his face or anything—see who this damn man is. I can only see his pants leg. I try to guess what cloth his trousers are made of.

With one hand, the man pulls my short gown up and with his knees forces my legs open. He sticks his thing inside. A sharp pain rips through my scarred belly as he pounds on me. I want to scream. I force my mouth shut. No moans, nothing. Got to save the babies.

After what seems like forever, I hear a groan and the pounding stops. Pushing harder on the pillow, he puts something cold on my neck, maybe a gun. He growls, "No talk. I can get those girls if you're here or not." His voice sounds like Johnny. It can't be!

The man gets off me. A small light comes on, a flashlight I guess, but the pillow covers my face so I still can't see him. The light goes out. For several minutes I lie quiet, shivering in fright. My body aches. My vagina throbs and stings like hell. I've been raped for sure. My neck is tingling. Taking a chance, I feel for the spot. My fingers come up wet. He cut me too. I jam my pillow onto the wound.

Finally, stretching my eyeballs I look around. He's gone. The pillow clamped to my neck, I get up, take a step and stumble over my suitcase. Getting my balance, I reach for the switch and turn on the light. My belongings are spread all over the floor. Guess he went looking for money before he got to me. I look at the babies. They are fast asleep. I cut the light and stumble into Susan's dark room. I run into her bed, waking her. I whisper,

"It's me. I've been raped." Susan flicks the light on and squeals, "What? God no!"

"Shush," I say, my finger to my lips. I nod yes. She grabs me and squeezes hard. Sobbing quietly, with one hand I hold on to her for dear life. We rock back and forth, not saying a word.

A few minutes later, we hear the boys come into the house. Susan lets me go and goes to the stairs to hush them. They come up stairs and Susan tells them, "A man broke into the house and scared Bernie." Before she can stop them, the boys head outside to search around the house. While bandaging my cut, Susan and I talk about what to do. She wants to call the police. I say, "I'm not sure, it hasn't done me any damn good."

"Sorry Bernie," she says. "He broke into my house. My kids live here. I'm getting the cops."

A half an hour later, two white police officers arrive. After telling them I was raped, they drive me to a police station. Once there, they take my name and address, then put me in a room alone. Sobbing, I wait. A half an hour later an officer gives me two shots. He says one is a 'morning shot' to prevent pregnancy. The other is for any diseases the rapist might have.

Alone again, I wait. After a while two other men come in and say they're detectives. The little one seems in charge. He starts asking me questions. "Where do you live? Where have you been? Who did you see? Why are you in Indianapolis? Your hairdo, you one of them Coloreds causing trouble? Who is Susan? What is your relationship to her? Does she have boyfriends? Are you married? Do you have boyfriends here? Are you a virgin? Have you reported being raped before? Have you been drinking?"

I give my answers, but I'm thinking, what do these questions have to do with rape? Married? A virgin? Boyfriends? My Afro? Do the cops think I didn't get raped? Or if I did, somehow it's my fault? It sure seems so.

Then the big cop asks me, "Can you say what he looked like?"

"No, I couldn't see him. It was dark."

"Did you try to resist?"

"No, I—I couldn't. He surprised me—was heavy and had a knife. I didn't want to wake the girls. So no I didn't—just wanted it over so he'd go away."

I start sobbing. I hate trying to remember what happened. But I have to: got to stop him from getting to Susan and her kids.

Handing me a tissue, the short detective takes over. He asks me who I've met since I got to Indianapolis. "Nobody, really," I say, "except—." I tell them about the taxi ride and that I had to get extra money out of my bra to pay. The officer frowns, looks at his partner and shakes his head in disbelief. As he writes down what I told him, I start thinking about the taxi driver. I'm sure he saw me go for my money. Also, he knew I was from out of town and where he dropped me off. Could it be him? I try to remember what he looked like. Other than being a Black man, I can't.

The officers want to go over what happened one more time. Again they ask me what I did to resist. Tired and frustrated, I bark at them.

"I told you. He was big—had a knife. He smothered me with a pillow. I couldn't breathe—couldn't move. He threatened the girls. I couldn't do anything."

Surprised, the big detective asks, "He smothered you with a pillow? You didn't say that before."

"Sorry, I didn't know it mattered. He was really heavy so—" Waving his hand at me, the big detective looks at his partner and says, "It's the pillow guy." His partner nods. "Again," he says. They both look at me and smile. "Okay. Sorry this happened to you," the little detective says.

I guess the police finally believe me, maybe even on my side. They tell me the 'pillow rapist' has attacked several women the same way as me. They also think the rapist was probably on the roof of the next house where he could see in the Florida room and where I slept in the little girls' room. Somehow, even though the back door was locked, he knew how to get in.

Back at Susan's, I try to sleep. I can't. I decide to stay in Indianapolis a bit longer. I need time to rest, get myself together and help Susan. She doesn't feel safe and is really worried about her kids. The rapist knows where the little girls sleep, so we move them to another bedroom and board up the door.

I try to be happy around everybody, put on an act for the kids. Alone, I'm a mess. Sobbing, I wonder, why me? What did I do to deserve this? Should I have done something different? Feeling unclean, I start taking lots of baths.

A few days later, I see a Black man hanging around the house next door. He could be the taxi driver. Scared but furious, I mutter, "Who cares, I'm going over there." I march over to confront him. He sees me coming and takes off. I chase him half way down the ally, but he disappears. Back at the house I tell Susan to watch out for him.

The next day I pick up my car and head home. It's a long drive, so I have time to think. I start to cry, making it difficult to see out of the windshield. I drive on, thinking about the rape, my life, and feeling unsafe again. About halfway to Oxford, I have had enough crying. Speaking out loud, I give myself a good talking to. "Well, Bernie, a nice little pity party you're having. So what? Maybe it's time for that. People think you're so tough and you are. But sometimes it's important to cry. But after that, you've got to go on and get past it."

Nearing Oxford, I sense my tears and scolding have done some good, helping me deal with this latest episode in my life. I'm wondering if I should tell someone about what happened. I mean; I'm not going to go around announcing, "Guess what happened to me? I was raped." But at least I could tell someone, not Terry, but maybe Mama, my beautiful mama.

Byran stayed with his great-grandmother while I was away. I can't wait to see him and hold him tight, but I'm still shook up and not ready to face him or anybody yet.

When I enter the house, I start blubbering again. There is nobody to comfort me or even talk to. The next thing I know, I'm standing in front of the bathroom mirror, wondering, can anybody see what happened to me? There is a bandage on my neck from the knife wound. Folks will see that for sure and ask about it; probably thinking Sammy is back. It will leave a scar of course. But it will mend. The real question is: can I heal what people can't see—my spirit, my heart, my soul?

I decide to take a bath, try to wash away the pain. Drawing the tub water, Mama's face flashes before my eyes. I don't know much about what happened to her in the past, just that she had it rough with Johnny. Still, I begin to think about her deeper that I ever have, so deep that I start feeling 'of' my mama. Family folks say I have a lot of her character. She says so too, sort of. We talk about things now. Mama tells me she always wanted to improve herself, go to college. Things just got in the way, babies, Johnny, whatever. She doesn't go into detail. Still, I know it's why she wanted me to stay with the Charles; have things she couldn't get. I wonder how Mama would handle what just happened to me?

I climb into the tub and start to scrub myself harder than I every have, hoping I can rub the invisible dirt off my body. Suddenly it hits me. I bet Mama has done this, tried to purify her body after being raped. I don't know why I think that except that somehow, some way she has 16 children. Actually, she had 18 babies, but two died in childbirth. I wonder if Mama had all of those children because she wanted them? Somehow, after what she told me about herself, especially what she wanted in life, I doubt it. I bet there were plenty of times when she didn't want to have sex. I bet lots of times she was forced into it and ended up with children—including me.

Wow, that idea shocks me. I'm thinking, girl, what an awful thing to say. But then I think about Mama's nature, her patience, so steady in her convictions and her truth. Even as a little girl in that Devil House, I knew she was paying a heavy price to be on this earth. Yes, she stayed with that devil Johnny, was part of his stuff. But I never disliked her. I just couldn't. I am like her in so many ways. I don't know how that is. Because of Johnny, I didn't grow up around her much. But people always tell me, "You are your mama 'featured out'." It's true; of all the kids I have her looks, her eyes, face, and body type. Apparently I have her mannerisms too. I guess that's not unusual. Even though she wasn't in Oxford, it seemed she was with me. When she did come to visit, it was like she made a special point to put herself in me. She would take hold of my chin and say, "You look up—don't look down. You don't have any reason to look down. If a person looks down too long it's not good. You don't have anything to be ashamed of."

Other times, when things were hard, she'd say, "Bernie, you stand tall. You will get through this. I did." I always wondered what she meant by "I did." She would never say. Maybe now I know. I bet Mama looked in her mirror and thought what I'm thinking, that I didn't do anything wrong for some man to do that, try to take my soul. Like me, I bet she told that damn mirror, "I am a strong woman. I can bear this, going to do what I need to do to get through. I will stand tall."

The water has cooled. Shivering, but full of 'Mama-daughter' pride, I climb out of the tub, dry, and dress. Walking past the bedroom mirror, I stop to check my hair. I'm exhausted so it must be an illusion, but Mama is smiling back at me. Tears fill my eyes. I blink and it's me in the mirror again.

I go get my little Byran. A big hug and he asks, "Mom, how is everything?" My heart is breaking. It's as if he knows something. I feel the tears coming, but I choke them back. It helps that my 'little man' is so happy to see me. He's very excited to have the car back. On the drive home, he says, "Nice going Mom. Now we can do more things again."

Yes, to my son Byran, I am the most wonderful person ever. It doesn't stop the pain, but it helps. 'Seeing' Mama, now a 'soul sister' in my struggle with rape, helps too, and maybe so much more. Of course, I don't tell Byran about—there's no need to right now, if ever. He's young and happy. Besides, we have so many other things to talk about and do.

A month later, Susan calls to tell me the Indianapolis police caught the pillow rapist. They say he raped at least one more woman. Choking up, I silently pray for my unknown 'soul sister.'

1970. The first gay pride parades tale place in various United States cities to mark the first anniversary of the Stonewall Riots that protested police raids on the Stonewall Inn, a well-known gay bar in New York City.

Chapter 27

Finding Louis Montrell

After some serious dating, Terry Robinson and I decide to get married. It's my junior year of college. I love Terry, and he loves me. He seems okay with Byran. That's all I'm going to say about that.

I should be happy. Here I am, twenty-five years old, have a beautiful son and good man in my life. I am in college working towards a degree. Everything is great, and I finally feel pretty safe. But there is still something gnawing at my innards. I miss my dad. No not that evil Johnny. I'm not crazy! I mean my biological dad. Louis Montrell is his name. He and Mama loved each other very much. At least that's what the story is. They should have gotten married and raised us kids together, but family jealousy and feuding got in the way. That's all I know.

Daddy's solution to the family trouble was to leave, join the military and go off to the Korean War. Mama quickly hooked up with Johnny. Daddy Montrell never came to Johnny's house to see us kids. I don't know why. Maybe he didn't want any part of that mess. So, except for a dark faded picture, I haven't seen him since I was three. No word from him either. He wasn't killed in the war—I know that much. Somebody, Mama or an aunt would have said so, I'm sure.

After I made the big decision to stay with Daddy and Mama Charles, I began to wonder more and more about Louis Montrell. It really bothers me that I don't know where he is, what he is doing and who he's with, if anybody. Does he think of us at all? If so, what are his feelings for me, Walter and the other kids? Does he know about Byran? Most important, does he know I still love him?

It's all so crazy. I know where Mama is, and Mama and Daddy Charles. I love them all so much. And Terry is here and in my heart. But my heart has plenty of room for my real daddy too. I need to find him. The problem is; how does one find a missing person, especially one gone for years? No one seems to know or isn't telling. Maybe it's hopeless but I'm not giving up.

*

Junior Bartles comes to my rescue. He is the Bartles' son. I know him a little because when I lived with Mama and Johnny, he would visit Vera Jo and Mr. Bartles sometimes. As a kid I didn't know that Junior's a homosexual. I do remember Johnny called him names I didn't understand: even threatened to beat him up if he ever saw him again. Junior didn't care. He kept sneaking over to the house with food for us. But then Junior stopped visiting his kin. Years later, Vera Jo told me he had moved to Cincinnati hoping city folks would treat him better. Now he owns a radio station, WCIN, I think.

One day, Junior and I are visiting our own families in New Miami. We are hanging at the Bartles' house. I don't think Junior knows Louis Montrell. But living in Cincinnati, where some of my mama's family are, maybe he can help me. I decide to ask him.

"Junior, I need to find my real daddy. It's driving me crazy. I know he is out there somewhere, but I don't know how to look for him." Junior is silent for a minute. Then he says, "If your dad is within two hundred miles or so of here, if anyone can find him it would be Little Abraham."

I know Little Abraham. Rather I know of him. He is a preacher. He has a religious radio program that Mr. McVey listened to as he tried to do us kids in. But I don't get Junior's point, so I ask, "What's Little Abraham got to do with finding my daddy?"

"Think about it Bernie. Little Abraham has a program on my radio station. Most of the Black folk in the Tri-State listen to him preach. I will have him announce that you are looking for your dad. If Louis Montrell is out there listening, he will hear it and hopefully contact the station. If he isn't listening, then someone may catch the program and know where he is or something about him. Maybe they will get in touch with him or the station."

"Really Junior?" I say. "Do you think it will work? Will Little Abraham do that for me?"

"As sure as his name is Isaac Jacob Swanson the Third. And it is, I guarantee it."

The next Sunday, Little Abraham makes the announcement on the radio. "Louis Montrell, if you are within the sound of my voice, someone is looking for you. If you hear this message, it is very important that you contact the station."

It works! My daddy is in a Cincinnati hospital listening to Little Abraham and hears the announcement. He asks someone at the hospital to call the station. Junior tells them Mr. Montrell's daughter Bernie is looking for him and gives them my phone number. That evening my daddy calls from his hospital bed. His voice is weak but joyful.

"Hello Bernie? This is Louis Montrell, your dad. I hear you are trying to reach me. Well, here I am, not in the best shape right now but I'm glad—"

His voice fades before I can answer. Holding the phone, I start screaming and sobbing, wondering why my daddy is in the hospital. Am I going to lose him before—?

A nurse comes on the phone and explains that Mr. Montrell is recovering from an operation, "He will be fine. Right now he is exhausted from all the excitement."

The next day I am at the hospital hugging my daddy. Feeling better, he tells me about hearing Little Abraham's plea.

"I nearly jumped out of bed. Somehow I knew it had something to do with you. I have been looking for you for so long. Your mother took you all someplace. Nobody in the family would tell me anything. I thought you didn't love me, didn't want to see me. Anyway, I shouted for the nurse and asked her to make the call. She did and they told her it was my daughter Bernie. And here we are!"

Along with Byran's birth, finding Daddy Louis is the most joyous day of my life. He wants to come to Terry and my wedding. As it approaches, I try to decide who should give me away: my real father or Mr. Charles. I finally choose Daddy Charles because of all he has done for me. Daddy Louis understands. He knows I love him. What a gracious, wonderful man.

On the wedding day, Daddy Louis beams from the front pew at me, his long lost daughter, as I say, "I do." Hopefully, this time with some idea of what I am doing.

1960-1980. Due to the racial integration of public facilities, a national wave of public swimming pool closings restricts Black citizens' access to swimming. At the same time, white flight to the suburbs brings the 'privatization' of swimming pools. The lack of opportunity to learn to swim results in a majority of Black children not being able to swim and three times more likely to drown than white children.

1973, May 8. Mr. Kenneth McDowell, Director of the Miami University Office of Minority Affairs says his office has been combating 'racial indifference' on campus, meaning there is a lack of institutional support for minority-sponsored activities. He says it is primarily due to Miami University's 'traditional, conservative role.' Black student enrollment at Miami has grown from 89 in 1969 to over 300 in 1973.

Chapter 28

Sink or Swim!

I'm in my senior year and preparing to graduate. There is only one problem. I am told in no uncertain terms that I have to learn to swim or I'm won't graduate from Miami University. Really? Oxford Blacks weren't really welcome at the public outdoor pool, so most of us, including me, didn't learn to swim. In fact I am really afraid of water, especially deep water. I've been praying for university officials to drop the swimming requirement, but they haven't. So now, in my final semester I'm taking swimming and lifesaving class, trying not to drown before I graduate. I get Miss Kile, the physiology professor who really admires my 'developed muscles,' as my swimming instructor. But in this class, she seems to have it in for me. Plus, she believes in the 'sink or swim' school of swimming instruction.

My so-called unique muscular body almost drowns me, not once but twice. Rather, Miss Kile almost drowns me twice. From day one, she is determined to make me float her way. She seems to have forgotten I don't have any body fat, so floating is totally impossible, at least horizontally. My floating is vertical, meaning my face is barely above water as my body dangles down below the water surface. This really frustrates Miss Kile. To her what I do is not floating, at least the way she understands it. For weeks, Miss

Kile keeps after me to float her way. I try, but in the end it's either dangle or drown.

In mid-semester, Miss Kile decides we are ready to save someone from drowning. She divides the students into two groups. Those to be rescued are to keep their clothes on and jump in the water. The others, the rescuers, are to strip down to swimming suits.

Miss Kile yells, "Bernie, get in the pool, Susan is coming for you."

I have never been in deep water with all my clothes on. Trembling, I go to the pool ladder, grab hold and slowly ease myself into 12 feet of water. Letting go, I push out toward the middle of the pool. Quickly, the wet clothes get very heavy, especially around my neck, arms and legs. The weight begins to drag me down. Terrified, I think, oh God, I'm going under for good! I try my best to dangle.

I see Susan jump in and swim towards me. Frantic, I start kicking and clawing to her as fast as I can. Susan stops swimming. She knows if I grab her I won't let go, that I will take her down with me. Panicked, Susan turns and starts swimming back to the side of the pool. "Hey get me! Don't leave! Don't lea—" I gurgle, my mouth filling with water. Exhausted, I gulp in air before I go under. Holding my nose, I feel my eyes bulging. My lungs are burning—I need to breathe.

Something suddenly grabs my arm and pulls me to the surface. A cloth-covered buoy is shoved in my face. I grab it and hang on for dear life. The girl who saved me, pulls me to the side of the pool. Other girls lift me out onto the pool deck. I'm coughing up water and trying to get my breath. I probably look like a beached black whale, but I don't care. At least I'm out of that nasty water. Miss Kile, hands on hips, stands over me, frowning. "Next," is all she says.

Man, I think, that's the cruelest thing ever. I'd sure like to pull Miss Kile into that water and sit on her head. Let's see how she likes drowning. But, of course I don't. I'm just glad to be alive. Thank you to whoever saved me.

*

Three weeks later, Miss Kile says we are ready to take the test again, this time from a boat in the middle of Hueston Lake. The same thing happens. Fully clothed, I jump from the boat, dangle a few seconds then start heading for the lake bottom. Again I have to be rescued.

The first time in the pool I was so thankful to be alive I didn't say anything to Miss Kile. But this time I'm mad as hell! Miss Kile is in another boat so I can't get to her. But once on shore, I tell that witch what I think of her, using words she probably never heard before or since. Miss Kile just laughs and tries to make it all seem funny in front of everybody. But I can tell her laugh is a nervous one. I am sure this 'physical specimen' with the developed muscles who's screaming at her from the top of her lungs scares her, makes her angry too. But I don't care.

Miss Kile will get back at me, that I know for sure. No doubt she will find some excuse to flunk me, preventing me from graduating. I know I should have kept my big mouth shut, but I couldn't. I'm so frustrated with myself and scared of the future, I go around muttering, "Damn girl, now what will you do if—"

As I'm trying to figure it all out, I get called into the Department Chair's office. The Chair heard about the two rescue episodes and wants to hear my side. After profusely apologizing for cussing out Miss Kile, I tell her what's going on and the situation I'm in.

A week later, I am assigned to a different swimming instructor. Thank goodness, Mrs. Cartright doesn't believe in the 'sink or swim' approach. Better yet, she's okay with my dangling way of floating. Best of all, after multiple tries, on the last day of the semester I pass my swimming test. For sure, I'm not going to the Olympics, but I can do a pool lap or two before I start dangling.

*

In June 1973, I graduate from Miami University with a degree in Health Science. I am one of the first Black students to graduate as part of the Equal Opportunity Program (EOP). The

Miami Student, our campus newspaper, wants to know about my experience at Miami. Thanks to Mr. Franklin Jacks, I tell the interviewer exactly what I think.

"Frankly, if I had had a better start, I would have been a better student. I'm glad it's over. The EOP will continue as the Blacks try to meet the white students halfway. But we are tired of trying to reach out with little in return."

At Commencement, Dr. John Hope Franklin, the famous African-American Studies scholar, introduces me to the audience and congratulates me on my achievement. I am the first of sixteen children in my family to graduate from high school and college. It is a wonderful day for all of us with plenty of happy tears and laughter, especially since my graduation cap looks silly pinned to the top of my Afro. I don't care; I made it, even if I can't float the right way. But floating through life the right way isn't exactly what I do well anyway.

1973. Tom Bradley becomes the first Black mayor of Los Angeles, California. Maynard Jackson is elected Mayor of Atlanta, Georgia, becoming the first Black mayor of a major city in the southern United States.

1975. The National Society of Black Engineers is founded at Purdue University, in West Lafayette Indiana.

Chapter 29

Looking Back, Going Forward

With my graduation from Miami and marriage to Terry, my life is changing, moving fast. Terry takes a high school coaching job in Cincinnati Ohio so we move there in July 1973. As a young couple starting out, we need more income so I take a production line job at the famous Keebler Cookie and Cracker Company. Yes, I have my degree but—. On my second day at work, for some reason I really have to pee nearly every hour, so I stop work and go to the restroom. Funny, but nobody tells me everybody must 'break' at the same time. Supposed to just hold it, I guess. I'm fired. A week later, my doctor says I'm peeing so much because I'm pregnant.

This pregnancy is so different from my first one. I know what's going on, how my body changes, what to look and feel for. Most importantly, I am married to the father so the baby is 'legit.' I don't have to put up with any nasty stuff from people on that. This time everybody is excited for Terry and me. Byran can't wait to have a little sister or brother to play with.

Again, the baby's birth is a scary time. I start to get contractions at home, but I make it to the hospital only to learn I have a breech baby. After a few scary moments, the doctor is able to turn the baby around in my womb. Yea! My body comes through again with no need for an abortion or C-section cutting into my belly scars. I told all those doctors I could do it. But, I think that's enough babies for a while. We name our baby boy, Benton.

During my pregnancy, I find myself thinking back on what I have come through. Sammy is Sammy, but he doesn't come around. Sometimes he calls and wants to talk to Byran. Except for one call, when he tells Byran he's not his dad, Sammy behaves himself best he can. It's sad, but I can tell his 'fast' life is getting to him.

As for Mr. Johnny McVey—I still hate him! But I'm a grown woman now. I know it's best for my mental health that I try to understand why he did what he did to us. As far as I know, he didn't drink alcohol. I would rather he had. At least I could say it was the alcohol screaming at me, punching, whipping, and cursing me. But it wasn't. It was just a lot of nastiness coming from him. From the talks we kids have had about Mr. McVey, we know as a kid his dad wasn't around and his mother abused him. From my psychology classes, I learned it's more than likely his mother had been abused too in ways that we knew nothing about.

Our aunts told us it was Johnny's mother's idea to starve us, get us kids out of the way. When Johnny didn't do what she wanted, didn't get the job done, she turned on him. I didn't see that, but some of my family did. I do know that when the twins lived with Mr. McVey and Mama, the boy, Johnny Lee was very mistreated, just like Walter was. But Johnny May, the girl, Mr. McVey loved her, said she was kind to him. I am happy for that. If he gave her a break, got past his own stuff, that's good. Why he couldn't do that with this little reddish-haired girl, or any of the rest of us, I don't know. Anyway, from what I know now, I think about letting go of my hate, maybe even forgiving him for my own peace of mind. I can't yet. I'll just keep working it over—.

It surely helps soften my heart about past things, even about Mr. McVey, to have my real daddy with me. We promised to never lose each other again. Best of all, a few months back, I get to see Daddy and Mama reunite. Walter and I drive him over to the house where all the bad stuff happened. Now in her sixties,

Mama still lives there, but alone. She is on the porch rocking, waiting. Daddy sees her and climbs from the car quick as he can. Poking the ground with his new cane, he hurries to the porch and up the stairs. They embrace for a long time. Walter and I watch in amazement. Finally, both our 'soul' folk are together, maybe even friends again. For me, it's the best thing that ever happened at that Devil House.

*

In 1976, Terry is hired as assistant football coach at Bowling Green State University, so we move just south of Toledo Ohio. I hate to say it, but Terry and I are drifting apart. Of course he is very busy with football, and I have two boys to look after. But a couple of times in Cincinnati, I get suspicious about some 'other woman' things, but decide not to mention them, just let it be. I do feel that Terry, although a good man, isn't ready to be much of a husband or father. In that way he is like Sammy, not paying a lot of attention to the kids or me. With Sammy and Byran, I had to grow up fast, had to take responsibility. As a young single man, Terry didn't have to. But now, he has a family, so it's time for him to be an adult. We talk about all this, and he promises to do better. Still, I find myself taking care of nearly all the family matters, living the 'patriarchal lifestyle' as my sociology professor would say. It's like I have three children in my house. Hopefully this won't last long. With my college education, I've got other things to do, including going for a Masters degree. So I'll bide my time, hoping things change for the better. I'm especially hoping the 'other woman' business isn't true.

*

We can't believe it! In 1977, Terry is offered an assistant coaching job at Purdue University with Coach Jim Young. Terry was a graduate assistant during Coach Young's career at Miami. Purdue is in the Big Ten Conference, and that's big time sports, especially football.

We move to West Lafayette, Indiana. Byran is in high school and is a great kid, especially in looking out for his new little brother. I start calling him Byransong, after a movie about two pro football players, one white, one Black who are close friends through the white player's losing battle with cancer. I don't know, for some reason the name fits my first boy. I wish Terry had more 'feeling' for Byran but—.

At Purdue, football is year round big business, so Terry is away more than ever. When he is around, his mind is not really with us. It's becoming clear that he and I still have a different idea of family life. I think he could help around the house and engage with the boys, especially sixteen-year-old Byran. Instead, Terry spends 'home' time reading about different religions, studying what they say about the 'meaning of life.' That's what he tells me, "I'm searching for the meaning of life." I stare at him and say, "Terry, look around, it's right here." So far, it doesn't seem to be good enough.

*

I wait two years, but nothing changes. I decide to continue my own search for 'life's meaning' in graduate school. I enroll in Purdue's Masters in Health Education Program. I love being back in school again, studying, thinking, and talking about new things. Byran has started at Purdue University too. Of course he's already gone though one undergraduate program with me, but this time it's his adventure. We love being at the university at the same time.

Things are getting worse between Terry and me. Our differences keep getting deeper, more serious. We begin to argue more, in fact most of the time, so home is not a happy place. Unlike with Sammy, there aren't any physical fights. It's more psychological, a lot of passive aggressiveness, the silent treatment, that sort of thing. It's just as exhausting. Terry has dropped his religious search for life's meaning. Now he wants to be s-o-m-e-b-o-d-y, someone important. I think big time sports can do that to you, if you let it. As one of the few Black couples at the university, we are very 'visible' and have many friends of all colors and professions. But it's not enough for Terry. He wants a flashy lifestyle, wants to be part of West Lafayette's high society. He wants me to quit school and go earn big money, be more outgoing and social. Well, I know who I am, what I want, so we argue. I tell him, "Man, you know that's not me. I can't fake it. I am who I am."

"Come on, you could change if you tried. If we had more money coming in, you could dress up, put a cocktail in your hand, and let me show you off to important people."

"Important people?" I mock. "Hey man, I've lived a little, struggled, faced r-e-a-l-i-t-y, been there for the boys—and YOU. That's what's important. We're important!"

So that's the big thing between us now. I hate to say it again, but in many ways Terry's still a child in a man's body. Meanwhile, I'm a student, mother, homemaker, and yes, substitute father. But, I'm afraid there's also something else going on. Let's just say that Terry, like Sammy, has a 'wandering eye' for women. It's hard to take, to believe. In many ways Terry is such a good man. I'm not in a life-threatening situation with him like I was with Sammy. He's not physical with me, or the boys. Most of all, Terry knows what I went through with Sammy and his women. He knows I'm not going for that again.

*

We go on like this for almost a year. Then sadly, we decide to separate and see if things can be worked out for the boys' sake, especially little Benton's. But they can't, especially since I hear he's got women at his apartment. So my suspicions are, well as I said, I'm not going for that. I told him what I want and that's not it. Worse, even though separated, all we do is argue, yell and grow further apart. Things get so bad between us that one night Terry almost kills us. Yes he does, and on purpose!

It happens after we attend an evening event at the university, you know, for show. Driving home we start arguing. Both of us are getting very angry, start yelling at each other. All of a sudden, Terry loses it and screams, "I'm going to end this right now bitch!" Grabbing hold of the steering wheel with both hands, he speeds up and swerves the car back and forth, back and forth over the two-lane highway. Looking ahead, I see headlights coming our way.

"Terry, stop it! What are you doing? Stop!" I scream. I want to grab the wheel, stomp on the brake, anything to get out of the way of those headlights. All I can do is scream. Terrified, my mind flashes back to Johnny, to Sammy, always making me have to fight them. Now it's Terry. It's like three devils are in the car with me!

Somehow, my screaming works. Terry stops swerving back and forth, straightens the car out, slows down, and stops on the side of the road. Two cars whiz by. We sit in silence, shivering, breathing hard, and trying to calm down. Terry is hugging, squeezing the steering wheel like he wants to crush it. He's staring at the floor, moaning. A flood of tears pours down my cheeks. I'm thinking, what just happened? Why is Terry so angry, so frustrated with me and with life that he wants to harm—to kill us? I don't know the answer.

Finally Terry lifts his head, lets go of the steering wheel, and says, "I'm sorry Bernie. I don't mean it." I stare straight ahead, sobbing, too upset and angry to say anything. More cars speed by. I catch myself wondering which one—.

"I'm sorry, Bernie," Terry says again. "You can stop crying, I said I'm sorry."

I erupt. "Damn Terry, you're sorry? Want me to stop crying? I don't want to stop! You know me—where I've come from, what I went through. Might as well put a damn gun up in my face and pull the trigger. I'M NOT DOING THIS AGAIN—EVER!"

Shortly after that awful night, my heart breaking for my boys, I file for divorce.

1983, November 3. Jesse Jackson announces his candidacy for President of the United States in the 1984 election. He is the second Black candidate to run a nationwide presidential campaign.

1985, May 13. Philadelphia police drop a satchel bomb on a row house occupied by members of MOVE, a Black Liberation and back to nature organization. Eleven Black citizens, including five children and MOVE leader John Africa are killed. The fire engulfs sixty-one houses and leaves 250 citizens homeless in the largely Black neighborhood of West Philadelphia and heightens tensions between government officials and Philadelphia's Black population.

Chapter 30

A Graduation for Two

Byran is heading towards the front door when I say, "Byran, could you stay home with Benton? I have to go get measured for my commencement cap and grown." Byran turns back to me and says, "Mom, that's where I'm going."

"Where?"

"To get my graduation outfit. I'm graduating in a couple of weeks."

"You are?" I say. "I thought, I didn't know you were all fin—"

I stop talking and stare at my son. He stares back. Suddenly we both know what is about to happen. We are going to graduate from Purdue University in the same year, no wait, on the same day: him with a Bachelors degree and me with a Masters. I have been so wrapped up with things, trying to finish my classes, post-divorce stuff and my job that I didn't realize it until now. He didn't either. We freak out!

"Oh my God, come here Byransong," I shout. "I want to kiss you all over. Oh my God, I can't believe it." Byran runs over, grabs me, bear hugs me, and covers my face with kisses. I do the same to him. Ten seconds later, we let go and start laughing, dancing, and jumping up and down all over the living room. "Mama," he shouts, "How did this happen? After all this time, who'd ever think—?"

"I don't know," I cut in, screaming. "I don't know, but it's going to!"

We start hugging and kissing again. I squeeze my baby boy, now my young man, as hard as I can. I'm wondering, how did this happen? What does it mean, if anything. Is it just a coincidence? Why wasn't I paying more attention?

Exhausted, we sit on the floor yoga style, looking at each other. We reach out to hold hands and start to cry. Tears on his cheeks, Byran blurts out, "Mama, can you believe it? We are going to finish together."

"Yes, Byran, we ARE going to finish together, just like we've been doing since you were born, even with things getting in the way or trying to stop us; some scary things and people you don't know about—"

Byran interrupts. "I do know Mama. Even as a little kid, I knew bad stuff was going on. I was scared a lot, but you were always there fighting. You pulled us through. You had to be strong and you were. Now too, with Terry, the divorce and all."

Embarrassed, I laugh nervously, not wanting to go there and spoil this moment. I wish I hadn't brought up the past, but it's done. Now we just sit giggling and shaking our heads in wonder.

"Hi Mama. Why are you guys on the floor laughing?" It's Benton. He's standing at the living room door, his big eyes staring at us like we're crazy.

"Come here baby," I say. "Mama and Byran just found out we are graduating from the university on the same day. So we're doing a little celebrating." Benton trots over. I pull him down on my lap. Folding him into my arms, I ask, "What do you think of that, little man?"

"I guess it's okay," Benton says quietly. He stares at the floor. Then, perking up, he asks, "Can we play more now?"

Taken by surprise, Byran and I look at little Benton, then at each other. Tears fill my eyes and roll down my cheeks. Wiping my wet face with the back of my hand, I say, "Yes, baby, we will have time to play. Plenty of time."

Byran and I look at each other, both realizing that our going to school and studying; along with my job and the divorce from his dad have been super hard on Benton. Our baby boy is lonely, feeling left behind by everybody. I'm crushed, knowing I have failed him. All I can do is hug him tight and say, "No way could we have done this without you little man. No way."

"We will do the same for you, Benton," Byran says. "When you graduate from college, we will be there. And Mama will always be there for you, just like she's been for me." I smile and nod yes at Byran. Squeezing my little Benton harder, I think, O Lord, can I do this again?

*

Commencement morning is here! Byran and I are floating in air. Neither of us could sleep a bit. We spent the whole night talking, eating and laughing with family and friends. Mama, Daddy Louis, my Walter and several other siblings are here. Mama and Papa Charles are here too, looking down on us from heaven, sharing in this wonderful occasion. It's amazing, truly amazing.

The whole university knows about our unique graduation. At 6AM, a Purdue University TV crew comes to our house. They interview everyone and film our family breakfast for a newspaper article and news program. Then it's time for Byran to go to his morning Commencement. Soon we all head out to campus.

I watch my Byransong strut across the stage, his head held high, to accept his Bachelor of Science in Hotel and Restaurant Management. A couple of hours later, he watches me, his mama, tear-filled eyes searching the sky, walk across the same stage to receive a Masters in Health Education and Research.

What a glorious day, I mean a GLORIOUS day. We couldn't ask for better weather, a better event, friends and family, better everything. He did it. I did it. We did it!

1952. George and Mary Lain Grosscup purchase the Oxford Ohio property that includes The Bluffs. As of 2021, The Bluffs remain the property of Dr. George Charles Grosscup III (Beau) and Frederic Bert Grosscup.

1981, February. Bill Withers and Grover Washington Jr. release the song *Just the Two of Us*. It wins the 1981 Grammy Award for best R&B song.

Epilogue

Just the Two of Us, Building Castles in the Sky

The second morning after that grand day, I awake to a new sound, a quiet house. "Wow," I say to my bedroom walls. Last evening my family left for home and friends went back to their own lives. The boys are also off doing different things. Byran is staying with friends, no doubt still celebrating his graduation. Benton is with Terry, supposedly for two days. It depends how things go. So, at least until I get a call from Benton wanting to come home early, I'm on my own. That's good because as a forty-year old Black woman, divorced, and a little boy to rear, I need to figure out where to go from here, what do I want to do and how to do it. Yes, I have my Masters degree, so that should give me more opportunity in the job market to get a professional position. No more picking up whatever job just to earn money. Byran is on his own, making his way too. He'll come if I need him, but most of the time he'll be gone. Benton is all mine. I made sure of that after he came home crying one too many times from what Terry said about his mama. Terry is still confused about what he wants. He has women around all the time and does a lot of drinking, even when Benton is there. I told the judge it was not fair to my son to be around Terry while his dad tried to grow up. "Terry's a good man, but a bad influence," is how I put it. Of course, as Benton's dad, Terry will be in my life forever, same as Sammy. But with Sammy, I finally got lucky. Once he learned he couldn't mess with us, Sammy pretty much disappeared. Byran never mentions his dad anymore.

With Terry, it's going to be different. He's on the fast track as a football coach. At any time, he could be offered a new job in a town far away. I will have to find a way to make it work. Probably go where he goes. I'll be damned if I'll let little Benton out of my sight. That boy needs his mama. And I need him.

A hunger pang hits my stomach, making my old belly scars tingle. Exhausted, I had slept till almost noon, so of course I haven't eaten since last night. I get out of bed, stop in the bathroom, then head to the kitchen, hoping some leftovers are still around. There's only a small piece of cake. "Damn, I should have known," I murmur, remembering how much my family can eat. I grab the cake, a glass of water, and sit down at the kitchen table. Staring into space, it hits me. Hey, for the first time in forever, I'm on my own, alone. No, not alone, got two kids. I guess the word is independent. No one is here to tell me what to do or me have to consider what they want, their feelings, and needs. It's just me. "Wow," I say. "What a difference. Wow."

As usual, little Miss Curiosity starts up with questions. What should I do? What do I want? Who should I be? Is being independent what I want? I already know the answers to the first two questions. I didn't go to graduate school just for fun. I want to start my health education profession right away.

It's the last two questions that get me thinking deeply. Who do I want to be? Well, a strong woman of course. People already say I'm strong, and I guess I was when I had to be—too often I'd say. But I've learned there are different kinds of strong. There's Mama Charles strong. I call it 'dignified' strong. But she had Daddy Charles to lean on, to talk to and be with. Great, but a 'Daddy Charles' is hard to find. I've tried twice. My 'warrior' sister Franny is a 'hard' strong. She had to be. Me too, but now I hope I can be a little 'softer' strong. Mama was very strong, a 'cause fighter,' at least until she came under Mr. McVey's spell. Alone now, she is a wonderful woman, but with deep scars from her time with him. After two husbands, I know for sure I'm not falling under any man's 'spell' good or bad. If that's strong, I'm it. It's being 'independent strong.' I mean, men are okay, fine really. But maybe it's also okay to be your own person in control of your life, doing what YOU want. Maybe women and men can be friends, not just messing with each other most of the time. Have to see about that.

I know other strong women of course. Aunt Mona was strong, a lot like Franny. The gray 'book lady' seemed that way, as did my Oxford librarians, some high school and college friends. I read about other strong women, Mrs. Roosevelt, Sojourner Truth and now Nina Simone. But it's hard to put myself in their shoes, not knowing enough about them and what makes them strong. I'll just keep reading about them, and others.

Wow, it's really difficult to know exactly what being a 'strong woman' means. Thank goodness, I have some 'models' to lean on. Until I figure it out, I'll just do what seems right for me. Of course, I can't know if I'll like being alone, I mean independent. Maybe I will for a while, maybe even for a long time. Again, I don't really know what being 'independent' means either, so I'll have to figure that out too.

*

For two days, I rattle around the house, doing what many people say is being independent. I do want I want, when I want, chores, fixing things, watering plants, reading, a little furniture moving, shopping, all on a whim. No asking permission or considering anybody else. Of course I'm listening to my music all the time, mostly R&B and jazz. I play Bill Wither's *Just the Two of Us,* over and over, trying to learn the words. I especially like the chorus line about 'building castles in the sky.' It reminds me of long ago when I would climb a tree or escape to the Bluffs alone, sort of my castle, to hide, cry, dream, and tell the trees, vines, rocks, and Bull Run creek what's going on in my Oxford world. What a great gift the Bluffs were to me. Trouble is, this kind of freedom seems selfish. I know myself, can't do it for long. If I'm independent, it's got to have heart, be deeper and have soul to it. It's got to be part of me, but what?

*

This morning I wake and realize Benton's time with Terry is up. Seems they got along okay or Benton would be back early. Anyway, my alone time is over for a while. It will be great to have the 'little man' here and maybe Byran too. I haven't solved that 'being independent' thing yet. Maybe that's why I didn't sleep well. Or it could have been the rape nightmare again. My neck feels like it.

I crawl out of bed, put on my robe and head for the bathroom. Finished doing 'my business,' I stand at the sink, washing my hands and looking into the mirror, wondering how I'm going to tame my hair before Benton and his dad get here.

"Back thinking about other folks, girl?" I ask my reflection. I laugh and say, "Of course you are. That's what you—" I stop talking as my brain flashes where it hasn't been for a long, long time, what it avoided, shut out. Weak kneed, I sink to the floor. Images race through my mind of that Devil House; of a little girl called Puke on her knees snipping grass with scissors, getting whipped with an ironing cord, eating food from garbage cans, flames burning up her belly, her little brown body wrapped in white gauze, and on and on. My body sags as I realize that little girl is still with me. I thought, yes prayed, I had left her behind, buried her under my books and degrees, my boys, Walter, Mama and Daddy, all the good things, all my triumphs. But she's still here, deep in my soul.

Tears soak my cheeks. Sitting cross-legged on the bathroom floor, I rock back and forth, moaning, silently wondering, why won't she let me be? What am I to do with her? How can I be free, move on if she won't let go? Is that her scratching on my belly scars all the time?

Slowly, the thought of little Bernie clinging to me for dear life begins to make sense. "Okay, I get it." I sob. "That little girl, she's fighting to stay in my soul where she's safe. That—that song about castles in the sky, no wonder I love it. I'm her castle, just like my trees, the Bluffs were for me. Not a real castle, just a safe place for a little girl—and a woman too!"

Closing my eyes, the image of a little girl in that Devil House that sent me crashing to the bathroom floor returns. But now I'm angry, ready to move on. I spit out some 'attitude.' "Get off the damn floor girl—do something!" Reaching for the sink, I pull myself to my feet with Franklin Jacks' words ringing in my ears. "You know about it. You don't like it. So what are you going to do about it?" "Yes, Mr. Jacks," I mutter. "That's why you went after me. Brave words are one thing, brave deeds, acts, something else."

Trouble is, looking in the mirror all I see is 'Bernie the phony.' Upset, my belly scars tighten as I think, what brave deeds? All you've done is forget that little girl, push her away. But you can't. You know too much, where she came from, what she came through, and what she did to get you—us here. Brave acts? SHE stood tall, told them what SHE wanted, fought every day for it. EVERY DAY! It's what strong independent women, those you admire so much, did, do for themselves, and others. It's what you've tried to do before, so what's different now? Just get back to it, starting with little Bernie, being proud of her, keeping her close. "C'mon girl," I hiss at the mirror. "Forget making her disappear. It's not happening—never, ever!"

My scars are calming down, so am I. But there's still Mr. Jacks' other questions; "What kind of education? What are you going do with it, once you get it?" Well, for damn sure I never wanted to remember that Devil House. But this morning, 'seeing' little Bernie there, I now realize what she needed, was desperate for. "That's it, Franklin Jacks," I say. "Safe places. That's what my Health Science degree is about. Little Bernie needed them. I still need them. As strong, as militant as you are Franklin Jacks, you need them too. We all need them, more Bluffs, more trees, more 'castles in the sky,' whatever. Safe places, I'll be a 'cause fighter,' a 'warrior' for them. That's what I'll do with it, about it,

Mr. Jacks. I'll tell them what I want, and do it. No more damn Devil House!"

*

"Mama, where are you?" It's Benton and maybe Terry. They're early. Forcing myself to calm down, I yell, "In here! Be there in a minute." I look in the mirror, grab a hand towel and try to fix up. Finally, I give up. I need to see my baby, so I head to the front room. When I arrive, Terry isn't there. Benton runs over, hugs me with all his might and says, "Daddy had to go, says hi."

"Hi back," I reply, kissing his little nose. He looks up at me, frowns and asks, "What's a matter Mama? Are you crying?"

"I have been, baby. Crying tears of joy—and triumph."

"I know what joy is, Mama. It's like happy. What's that other word?"

"Triumph? You'll find out soon enough, little man. And like your mama, you won't ever forget it. C'mon now, let's see how far up that old oak tree we can go this time."

The End of the Beginning

Table of Figures

Page 56: *Youth March for Integrated Schools*, 25 October 1958. Courtesy of National Archives

Page 66: Ohio Civil Rights Commision logo, https://en.wikipedia.org/wiki/Ohio_Civil_Rights_Commission

Page 72: *Walgreens Lunch Counter Protests*, four shown from left are Joseph McNeil, Franklin McCain, Billy Smith and Clarence Henderson. Jack Moebes/News & Record, https://www.charlotteobserver.com/news/local/article239561018.html

Page 78: *Aftermath of mod attack on Freedom Riders traveling by bus, Anniston, Alabama*, May 14, 1961, Courtesy Birmingham Civil Rights Institute, https://www.blackpast.org/african-american-history/freedom-rides-1961/

Page 86: Onaway Elementary School sign, coutesy of author

Page 96: *W.S. McIntosh making remarks on the steps of Dayton City Hall*, Aug. 2, 1962. Photo: Paul Horn, Dayton Daily News, https://www.daytondailynews.com/news/local/dayton-civil-rights-pioneer

Page 102: From an article in darrtown.org, The Talawanda School District, https://darrtown.org/organizations/schools/talawanda-school-district.html

Page 108: From an article in clarionledger.com, *History: Freedom Riders Arrested* by Jerry Mitchell, Mississippi Department of Archives and History, https://www.clarionledger.com/story/news/local/journeytojustice/2016/05/24/history-freedom-riders-arrested/84850930/

Page 112: From https://bchistoricalsociety.com/2017/09/15/history-butler-county-childrens-home-topic-historical-society-talk/

Page 120: From an article in aaihs.org, *Poll Power: A New Book about the Voter Education Project* by J.T. Roane, https://cdn.aaihs.org/2019/05/poll-power-e1557246379456.jpg

Page 124: From a collection of images called Hospitals 3 at http://www.cincinnativiews.net/images-2/State%20Hospital-Carthage.jpg

Page 128: Courtesy of the author Laverne Merritt-Gordon

Page 134: From an article in Young Gifted Sistah, *Freedom Summer Chapter One: There is a Moral Wave Building* by Megan Sims, https://younggiftedsistah.wordpress.com/2015/03/17/freedom-summer-fs-chapter-one-there-is-a-moral-wave-building/

Page 142: From an article in the Newak Advocate, *Advocate at 200: The Cincinnati Race Riots from 1967* by Staff Reports, https://www.newarkadvocate.com/story/news/local/2020/06/13/advocate-200-cincinnati-race-riots-1967/5332783002/

Page 150: From an article in The Enquirer, *A Decade-by-Decade Look at How Avondale Came Back After the 1968 Riots* by Mark Curnutte, https://www.cincinnati.com/story/news/2018/04/04/decade-decade-look-how-avondale-came-back-after-1968-riots/394991002/

Page 158: From an article in The Guardian, *'Stereotypes of the Black Panters Are Far From the Truth': Marching in Philadelphia, 1971* by Candice Pires, https://www.theguardian.com/artanddesign/2016/nov/25/stereotypes-black-panthers-philadelphia-1971-khalid-raheem

Page 164: From an article on bet.com, *This Day in Black History: Nov. 7, 1972* by Jonathan P. Hicks, https://www.bet.com/news/politics/2013/11/07/this-day-in-black-history-nov-7-1972.html

Page 172: Shirley Chisholm campaigning for president in 1972. Courtesy of Arlie Scott. From an article in People's World, Shirley Chisholm: Unbought & Unbossed by Special to People's World, https://www.peoplesworld.org/article/shirley-chisholm-unbought-and-unbossed/

Page 176: From an article on cnhi.com, *Journalists Push For Federal Shield Laws, Protection of Sources* by Jim Zachary, https://www.cnhi.com/featured_stories/journalists-push-for-federal-shield-laws-protection-of-sources/article_d6f22750-7f6b-11e6-9b02-73e8590d3064.html

Page 184: A scene from the Stonewall Riots, June 28, 1969, https://i.imgur.com/Vdb0uLl.jpg

Page 190: Children play at the Marcus Garvey Mini-Pool in New York City, 1967Jeff Wiltse. From an article on wnpr.org, *A History of Racial Disparity in American Public Swimming Pools* by Carlos Mejia, https://www.wnpr.org/post/history-racial-disparity-american-public-swimming-pools

Page 196: From Black History Los Angeles, https://lasentinel.net/black-history-los-angeles.html

Page 204: From an article on phillymag.com, *Can Philly Fix the Block It Razed, Then Shabbily Rebuilt, After MOVE Bombing?* by Jared Brey, https://www.phillymag.com/news/2016/11/21/move-bombing-redevelopment-authority/

Page 208: Courtesy of the author Beau Grosscup